LORE and LURE
of OUTER SPACE

Allegory of Astronomy with the Greek muse of astronomy, Urania, and the
Alexandrian astronomer Ptolemy, designed by Johann Santritter, from
Sacrobusto's *Sphaerae mundi*, printed by Bonetus Locatellus, Venice, 1490

LORE and LURE

of

OUTER SPACE

by

ERNST and JOHANNA LEHNER

TUDOR PUBLISHING COMPANY
New York

To EVA MARIA WEININGER
and Her Angel Himmelblau

LIBRARY OF CONGRESS CATALOG NUMBER: 64-14860
PRINTED IN THE UNITED STATES OF AMERICA

CONTENTS

Sibyl, from Johann Lichtenberger's *Prognosticatio*, printed by Nicolas and Dominico dal Jesus de Sandro, Venice, 1511

INTRODUCTION

At the dawn of human history, when primitive man ventured out of his lair and looked at the small patch of world that surrounded his family cave, he encountered an assortment of plants which he could strip of herbs, leaves and fruit for his daily need of food. He also discovered a few species of animals, some of them dangerous to him which he learned by instinct to avoid, and others which he could catch, kill and eat. And his sluggish powers of observation and thought eventually gave him the vague idea that, as leader of his little band of companions and offspring and master of his small domain, he was in fact the unique center of the world. But when he explored behind the farthest boulder and brush of his personal universe, or crossed the hills or streams bordering his realm, he discovered other would-be sovereigns of his own kind, with their own personal universes. He warred with these interlopers and killed them if

Fanciful representation of the unfettered elements of chaos, from Robert Fludd's *Utriusque Cosmi Historia*, Oppenheim, 1617

~ 7

The Lord as World-creator, from Martin Luther's *Biblia*,
published by Hans Lufft, Wittenberg, 1534

he could, but if he could not he did the next best thing — he joined them. And soon man came to the conclusion that not he, in his singularity, but his whole species banded together was the hub of the larger world which he had discovered. Much later he took the next step in his egocentric evolution and decided that the earth, since it harbored such a splendid creature as man, must be the pivotal point of the universe. The celestial phenomena of sun, moon and stars, moving slowly over the firmament, were so remote and unimportant in his mind that they were not even considered to be bodies of any kind. But slowly man discarded the concept that these heavenly lights were just hanging there in the sky for no reason at all, illuminated by some inexplicable means. His searching mind, gradually becoming more and more organized, discovered that all these lights behaved in a somewhat orderly manner, moved and changed, vanished and recurred in a precise rhythm, not only from the light of day to the dark of night, but also according to longer seasonal spells of warm and hot, cool and cold weather. He found that when these star lights returned after a certain period to the same positions and exact formation they had

P'an Ku, the legendary son of chaos and architect of the Chinese universe, creating the world from granite rocks floating in space, from an old Chinese pen drawing

before, the same climatic conditions also returned. By counting the number of days and nights it took the stars to complete their cycle, he learned that he could rely on the rhythmic precision of their wanderings; and his growing powers of deduction slowly developed the theory of the calendar with its days, weeks, months, seasons and years. But man also pondered over the reasons for these mysterious heavenly lights and the nature of the guiding powers behind them. And to calm his fears of the unknown he invented supernatural beings patterned after his own magnificent self, but endowed with unearthly powers: the gods and deities which managed the changes in nature on earth and in the heavens, for the benefit or the disadvantage of mankind. In nearly every early belief and religion, the earth, created out of the abysm and the waters of chaos, became the primeval mother goddess. In union with the father god as personification of the supernatural powers of the universe, the mother goddess bore offspring, who in turn became the representative powers of the sun, the moon, the planets, the constellations and the diversified happenings of nature itself. And since man's life was influenced by the good and bad will of all these deities, he conceived the idea that his life was also guided by their visual celestial representations. Thus the foundation stone of astrology was laid. We owe to the cultures of Chaldea and Babylonia the first attempts at an organized science of astronomy-astrology. These were followed by the systems of Greece, Persia and Arabia. The cultural centers of far-away China, India and ancient Mexico also developed their own brands of astrological astronomy, independently of the Near Eastern—Mediterranean centers.

The Sun and the Moon discussing the Powers of the Firmament, from *Dialogus Creaturarum Moralisatus*, printed by Gerard Leeu, Gouda, 1480

The Story of Astronomy

In antiquity the science of astrological astronomy rested in the hands of scientist-priests. These astronomers developed the theory that the earth was a flat disk floating in the waters of the ocean from which it was originally born. The sun, the moon, the planets and the constellations, arising daily or nightly from the waters of the east, wandered on their eternal paths over the cupola of the sky to set in the waters of the west, from which they returned through the nether world to the east to rise again. This concept was inherited by the Greeks, whose philosophical genius led them to the theory of a mechanistic system of the universe — a theory ultimately crystallized by the Greco-Egyptian astronomer Claudius Ptolemy (2nd century A.D.), who constructed his famous *celestial sphere* in Alexandria. Ptolemy systematized the idea that the earth was not flat, but globular, and in fixed position at the center of the universe, with the sun,

The Alexandrian astronomer Claudius Ptolemy with his celestial sphere, from the Italian edition of his work *La Geographia,* printed by Nicolo Bascarini, Venice, 1547

Egyptian cosmos, depicting *Geb* — Earth, *Shu* — Air, and *Nut* — Heavenly Vault, who carries the barges of the sun on her star-studded back

Ancient Japanese cosmogram, representing the earth as a square surrounded by the waters of the ocean depicted as a circle

the moon, the planets and the constellations orbiting in circles around it. Ancient Rome made no contribution to astronomy other than to substitute Latin names and expressions for the Greek; astronomy was considered by the Romans to be a worthless trifle and a waste of time. When the Roman Marcus Fabius persuaded Gaius Julius Caesar to reform the calendar in 46 B.C., he had to bring the Greek mathematician and astronomer Sosigenes to Rome from Alexandria to assist with the astronomical calcula-

tions. In this calendar, called the *Julian Calendar*, after Julius Caesar, the ordinary year had 365 days, and every fourth year (leap year) 366 days, with the months placed as we know them today. This calendar was used by the Romans until the fall of the Roman Empire. In 325 A.D. it was accepted by the first Nicene Council and was used in the Christian Church without interruption until 1582. In that year it was superseded by the slightly reformed *Gregorian Calendar*, introduced by Pope Gregory XIII to

Christian concept of the World Soul, *Anima Mundi*, with the four elements, and Christ as the Primal Man, *Anthropos*, France, 1487

Ancient Mexican cosmological symbol of the movement of the universe, hieroglyphic sign from a wall carving

Peruvian Incan cosmogram, representing the sun as the center, the condors of the compass points, and the circle of the horizon

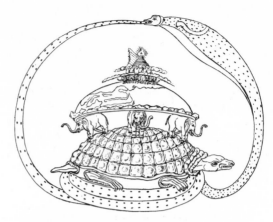

Hindu cosmogram, showing the tortoise, *Akupara,* supporting elephants upon which the earth rests, enclosed by the world-serpent

eliminate a displacement of ten days in the Julian Calendar against the astronomical year. This displacement had accrued over a period of 1257 years of the calendar's unchanged use since the Nicene Council accepted it. During the 8th and 9th centuries, when Europe was in the strangling grip of the Dark Ages, all science, including astronomy, deteriorated into mystical charlatanry and magical fraud. Only a handful of dedicated monks, sheltered from the law of the mailed fist behind the walls of a few mon-

asteries, tried to keep a glimmer of ancient knowledge aflame. At the same time, the Arabs were building their empire from the Straits of Gibraltar to the plains of Central Asia, and their emirs and kaliphs encouraged all scientific research and knowledge to the utmost. For the first time in history the Arab scientists in their far-flung empire were in a position to assemble, compare and integrate the accumulated scientific knowledge of the West and the East. With the acceptance of the Hindu numerals, which

Hopi Indian sky god, *Tunwup,* depicting the compass points, the sun rolling over the sky vault, and the movement of the universe

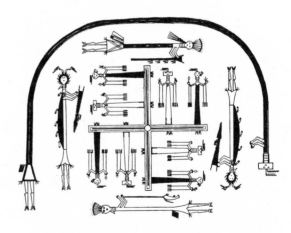

Navaho Indian cosmos, showing the compass cross, the swastika of sky revolution, and the gods of rivers, mountains and rain

contained the number *zero,* Arab mathematicians were able to develop the decimal system and replace the clumsy and tedious letter-numerals of the Eurasian mathematical systems. With these new numerals (today erroneously called *Arabic* instead of *Hindu numerals*) the Arabic scientists opened new vistas for all mathematical sciences, including astronomy. In the following centuries, Arabian astronomers, mathematicians, physicians and herbalists became the leading scientists of their time. The *Ptolemaic System* of the universe was accepted by both

The Arabic astronomer Messahalla, by Albrecht Dürer, from
Stabius' *Scientia,* Nuremberg, 1504

Italian astronomers with their instruments, from Anianus' *Compotus*,
printed by Andreas Freitag, Rome, 1493

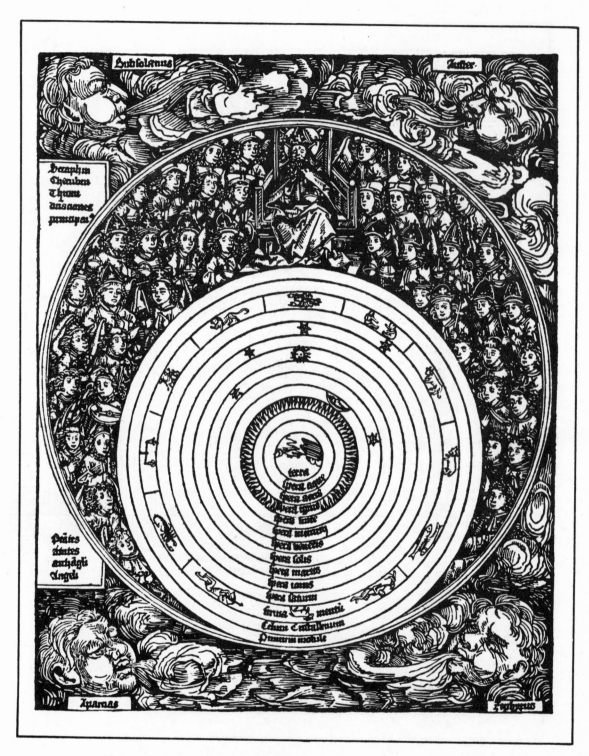

Christian conception of the universe, embraced by the realm of God and
His angelic court, by Michael Wolgemut, from Hartmann Schedel's *Liber
Chronicarum,* printed by Anton Koburger, Nuremberg, 1493

Arabs and Europeans as correct until the days of the Polish astronomer Nicolaus Copernicus (1473-1543), who originated the *Copernican System*. This was a revolutionary hypothesis in which the earth was not the center of the world, but a planet revolving along with the other planets and constellations around the sun, the real hub of the universe. With this theory Copernicus became the founder of modern astronomy. It is astonishing to realize that from Chaldean times up to the Middle Ages astronomers determined their measurements and data in such precise

Discussion between Theologian and Astronomer, from Alliaco's *Concordantia Astronomiae cum Theologia*, Erhard Ratdolt, Augsburg, 1490

Astronomical instruments, from Petrus Apianus' *Folium Populi,*
engraved by Hans Brosamer, Ingolstadt, 1533

order with only the help of geometrical stone structures such as steps and ramps of astronomical temples, pyramids and obelisks, and such primitive instruments as wooden or bronze cubes, squares, triangles and graduated circles. Yet with these they were able to chart the movements of the celestial bodies. The Danish astronomer Tycho Brahe (1546-1601), who invented the mural quadrant, improved many of the mechanical instruments of his

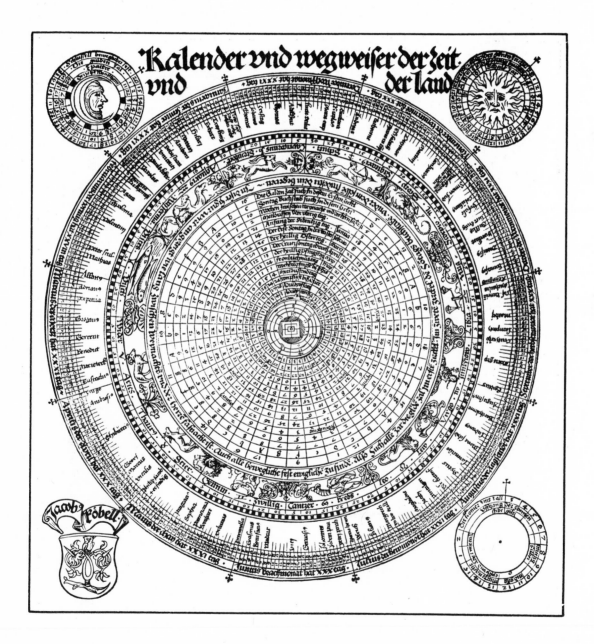

The Roman Julian calendar, from a broadside printed by Johannes Köbel,
Oppenheim, Germany, 1520

Tycho Brahe with his instruments in his Castle of Uraniborg, from his *Astronomiae Instauratae Mechanica*, printed by Levin Hulsi, Nuremberg, 1598

time. In recognition of his achievements Frederick II, king of Denmark, granted him the island of Hven, ten miles from Copenhagen. There he built an observatory, the Castle of Uraniborg (Fortress of Heaven), which became the gathering place of leading astronomers and philosophers. In 1590, the Dutchman Zacharias Jansen developed the basic principle of the telescope. In 1608, his compatriot, the glass-grinder Jan Lippershym, manufactured the first usable telescope. The most outstanding physicist and astronomer at that time was the Italian Galileo Galilei (1564-1642). In 1609 he improved the Jansen-Lippershym telescope for his own use, and with it discovered Jupiter's satellites, Saturn's rings, the sun's spots, and the phases of Mercury, Mars and Venus. With this instrument he demonstrated the truth of the Copernican System; but due to ecclesiastical and civilian opposition he was condemned by the Inquisition for heresy and forced to renounce his astronomical findings. Nonetheless astronomical knowledge marched on with seven-league boots throughout the following centuries. The Polish astronomer Jan Hevelius (1611-1687) discovered and constructed from his observations many of our modern constellations. The English mathematician and natural philosopher Isaac Newton

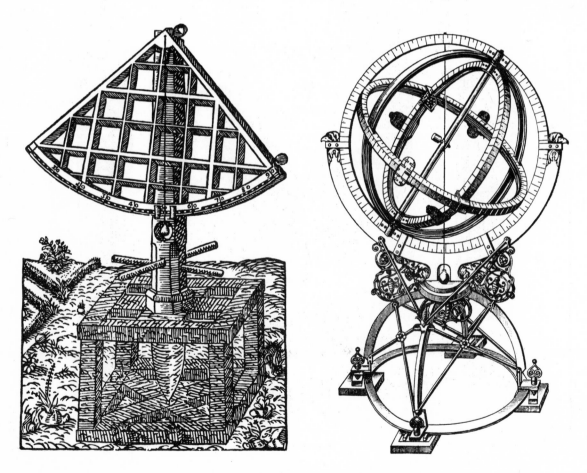

Tycho Brahe's quadrant, from his *Astronomiae Instauratae Mechanica*, printed by Levin Hulsi, Nuremberg, 1598, and an old reproduction of his equatorial armillary sphere

Contemporary portrait of Galileo Galilei, mathematician and astronomer
to the Grand Duke of Tuscany, from *Siderius Nuncius*, Florence, 1610

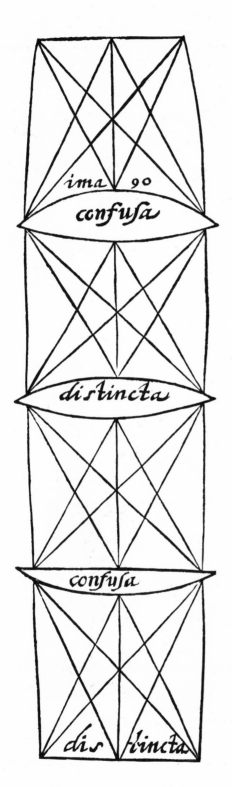

(1642-1727) discovered the law of gravity and the fundamental properties of light. His compatriot, the mathematician and astronomer Edmund Halley (1656-1742), computed the orbit of the Comet of 1682, and charted its many recorded appearances back to the year 11 B.C. His name became immortalized in HALLEY'S COMET. The Anglo-German astronomer Sir William Herschel (1738-1822), first president of the Royal Astronomical Society, constructed

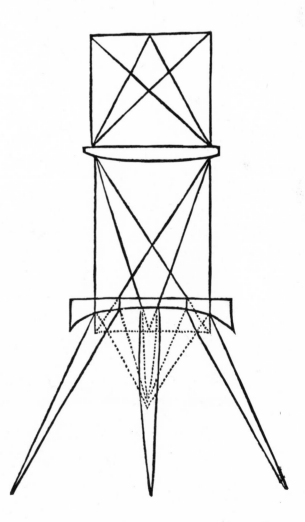

The optical principle of the first telescope, invented in 1590 by Zacharias Jansen, manufactured in 1608 by Jan Lippershym of Holland, from Peter Borelli's *De Vero Telescopie Inventore*, 1655

a 40-foot-long telescope, and discovered with it the first of our modern planets, URANUS, and about 5,000 new nebulae, nebulous stars and planetary nebulae. The second modern planet, NEPTUNE, was discovered in 1846 by the German astronomer Johann Gottfried Galle (1812-1910), as a result of computations by the French astronomer Urbain Jean Joseph Leverrier (1811-1877). The English astronomer John Couch Adams (1819-1892) had also calculated the position of Neptune independently with similar results. This discovery is regarded as one of the greatest triumphs in mathematical astronomy. The Italian astronomer Giovanni Virginio Schiaparelli (1835-1910) discovered in 1877 the *canali,* the CANALS OF MARS. In the same

year, the French Astronomical Society was founded by Camille Flammarion (1842-1925), who popularized astronomy by divesting it of much of its scientific terminology. On March 13, 1930, the American astronomer C. W. Tombaugh, working in the Lowell Observatory at Flagstaff, Arizona, discovered the third, and for the time being, the last of our modern planets, PLUTO. This was the result of research and predictions made in 1905 by the American astronomer Percival Lowell (1855-1916). With the growing interest in space, and the ever-increasing sums of money that are being spent for space research today, no one can foresee what further discoveries in our celestial system the future may bring.

Allegoric representation of Astronomy, after a French engraving
by Etienne de Laune (1519-1583)

Reaching for the Stars

Since earliest times the impression that the celestial dome has made on the human mind has been tremendous. The sky is so immense and so out of reach that nearly all ancient beliefs located in it or near it not only the habitat of their deities, but also the abode of the spirits of their dead. If man himself were unable to fly and soar into heaven, his winged soul could do so after his demise. At various times man likened this soul to the Egyptian human-headed soul-bird *Ba,* which after the death of the body flew to the gods; or to the butterfly-winged *Psyche* of the Greeks, the soul-butterfly of the Far East, or the winged angels of the Western world. Man's eternal quest for a better life also turned his mind to the inscrutable sky; and many an ancient philosophy and religion included the belief in a much better afterlife somewhere in heaven, where man's de-

The Flight of Daedalus and the Fall of Icarus, engraved by Albrecht Dürer, from Friedrich Riederer's *Spiegel der wahren Rhetorik,* Freiburg/i.Br., 1493

GENESIS Cap. XI. v. 4.
Scenographia Turris.

I. Buch Mosis Cap. XI. v. 4.
Der Perspectivische Riß des Thurn.

The Tower of Babel, from J. J. Scheuchzer's *Physica Sacra*,
printed in Augsburg, 1732

parted soul, unhampered by the ills and pains of his vulnerable body, would live in eternal youth, joy and pleasure. Such was the Persian *Paradise,* from the Persian *paira* — around, and *daeza* — walled, also called *Yima's House,* the walled celestial garden of the Persian folk hero *Jamshid,* the abode of the blessed souls. This concept was adopted by the early Greeks as their beautiful meadow *Elysium* on the banks of *Oceanus* where the sky begins: a land without snow, storms or rain, where the chosen lived in perfect happiness, partaking of the fare of the gods. Here they ate *ambrosia,* which preserved them from decay, and sipped *nectar,* the drink of immortality. The concept of paradise was also accepted by the later Hebrews and early Christians, as the celestial place where the souls of the saintly departed were received into heaven to live as angels, playing music on the harp and singing psalms and chorals. The Mohammedan paradise was similar, a celestial land where the souls of the departed believers were dressed in the green silk of the Prophet, where grapes were always within reach and beautiful *houris* waited on the faithful. The

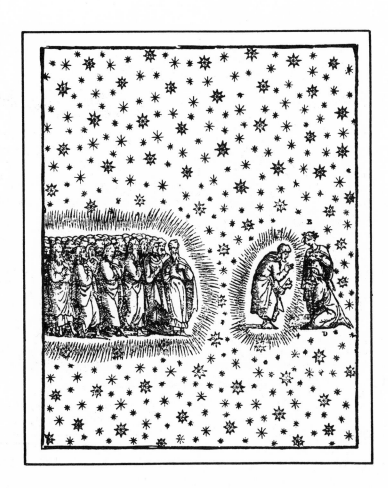

Dante and Beatrice entering the Heavens, engraved by Baccio Baldini, from Dante Alighieri's *Divina Comedia,* printed by Nicolo Lorenzo, Florence, 1481

Nordic heaven was *Asgard*, from the Nordic *ass* —god, and *garther*—court, or yard, the palace of *Odin*, containing *Valhalla*, from the Nordic *valr* — slaughter, and *höll* — hall, where the souls of the slain warriors were served and entertained by the *Valkyries*, the battle maidens. The belief in a happy afterlife in a celestial paradise is also reflected in Asiatic and American Indian religions. There is the *Secret Lake of Lotuses*, where the souls of the departed Chinese Buddhists sleep in lotus buds until the time when they are admitted to the celestial *Western Heaven*. There

is the *Happy Hunting Grounds* of the North American Indians, where peace and quiet reign in daytime, while at night the souls gather around the campfires of the stars to dance, smoke and gamble. There is *Qudlivum*, the Eskimo's happy spirit land in the sky, replete with food, games and pleasure for all who have died in childbirth, had fed the poor during their lifetimes, had known starvation, were murdered or committed suicide; also the abode for the self-sacrificing old who in times of food shortage had denied themselves so there would be more for

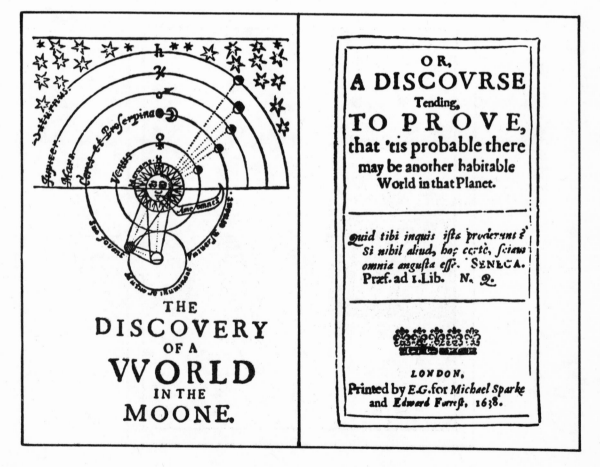

Frontispiece and title page from Bishop John Wilkins' *The Discovery of a World in the Moone*, London, 1638

the young. In some beliefs the souls wandered into heaven over the Milky Way, and in others over the rainbow. But it was not just his soul that man wished to elevate to heaven; mythological, religious and literary fables are full of legendary attempts of man to reach the sky not only spiritually, but physically. In Babylonian mythological legend, the erection of the *Tower of Birs-Nimrud* at Borsippa, reported also in the Old Testament as the *Tower of Babel,* was attributed to Nimrod, son of Cush, king of Babylon, who wished for greater power and decided to make war on God. His tower of bricks was built by 600,000 slaves on the plains of Birs-Shinar, and was so tall that it took a year to reach the top. From the summit the archers of Nimrod shot arrows into the sky which came back bloodied. When Nimrod ordered the continuation of the construction, God sent seventy angels to confuse the tongues of the workmen. One could no longer understand the next; they fought and some were transformed into apes and demons, while the survivors were scattered as the seventy nations on the face of the earth. One third of the

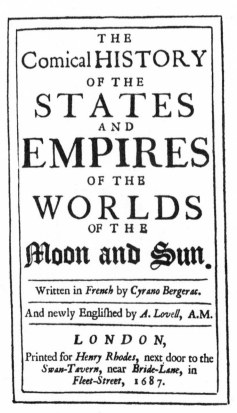

Frontispiece and title page from the first English edition of Savinien Cyrano de Bergerac's
L'Autre Monde, voyage interplanetaire et imaginaire, Englished by A. Lowell, London, 1687

tower sank into the ground, one third was burned, and the remaining third collapsed into a mountain of rubble. Whoever passed the place where the tower formerly stood lost his memory forever. Man realized early that if he were to reach the sky physically it was necessary to find some artificial device which would enable him to overcome his earth-bound existence. Thus, in Greek mythological legend, *Daedalus*, the sculptor and architect of the Labyrinth of Minotaurus at Knossos in Crete, fashioned wings for himself and his son *Icarus* so they could flee from the court of Minos. He warned his son not to fly too close to the sun, but Icarus, giving no heed to the admonitions of his father, soared too high, and the heat of the sun melted the wax which held his wings together. He fell to his death in the *Icarian Sea,* which was named after him. Throughout the following centuries the flight into space and the landing in paradise or on the moon became a favorite subject with many an early science-fiction writer whose works are part of world literature. In 165 A.D. the Greek satirical author, Lucian of Samosata, wrote the first known tale of a

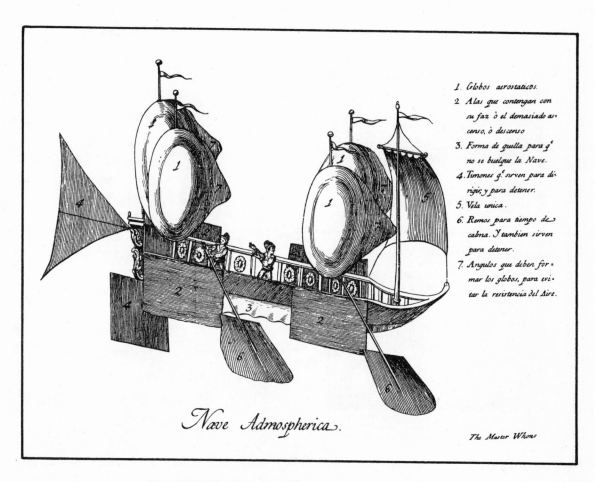

1. *Globos aerostaticos.*

2. *Alas que contengan con su faz ò el demasiado as- censo, ò descenso*

3. *Forma de quilla para q' no se buelque la Nave.*

4. *Timones q' sirven para di- rigir, y para detener.*

5. *Vela unica.*

6. *Remos para tiempo de cabna. Y tambien sirven para detener.*

7. *Angulos que deben for- mar los globos, para evi- tar la resistencia del Aire.*

Nave Admospherica.

The Master Whons

Nave Atmospherica, a fanciful design for a dirigible airship, from a Spanish engraving printed in Madrid, 1783

flight to the moon. His interplanetary explorers were swept off the earth in their ship by the force of a giant waterspout, and proceeded to the moon under full sail. The Italian poet, Dante Alighieri (1265-1321), related in his *Divina Comedia* his dream journey into the world of the souls, accompanied by Virgil through hell and purgatory, and by Beatrice through the happy sphere of heaven. In 1638, the bishop of Chester, John Wilkins, published his quaint work, *The Discovery of a World in the Moone*. In 1657, two years after the death of the French dramatist, poet and notorious duelist Savinien Cyrano de Bergerac (1619-1655), his work *L'Autre Monde* was published in Paris —— a fantastic tale of space travel in which the explorer was boosted into the firmament by a chain reaction of rockets to reach a paradisaic region where the beds were made of gigantic flowers and roasted larks rained down from the sky. The narrator later also reached the sun, where the Parliament of Birds assembled. Many artists envisioned and designed all kinds of fanciful aeronautic vehicles for trips into the sky before, in 1783, two French scientists, the

Fanciful design of a curious electrical flying machine by C. Boissel, Paris, 1775

First ascent by Charles & Robert Montgolfier in a manned balloon, Paris, December 1, 1783

brothers Joseph Michael and Jacques Etienne Montgolfier, invented the first lighter-than-air balloon, elevated first by the rising power of hot air and then by hydrogen gas. After their successful flights the race to conquer the skies physically was on in earnest. In the year 1804 Napoleon Bonaparte ordered the construction of a fleet of giant montgolfiers, able to carry an army of 3,000 men with horses, cannons and war equipment for an air invasion of England. The fleet never left the ground. In 1860, the French novelist Jules Verne (1828-1905), doyen of modern science-fiction writers, a man endowed with a highly technical mind and an uncanny prophetic fantasy, wrote his science-fiction books about space travel, *De la terre à la lune*, and *Autour de la lune*. The first American edition of these books, *From the Earth to the Moon, and a trip Round it*, was published in 1874 by Scribner, Armstrong & Co., New York. Verne selected as launching site for his space projectiles, of all the places on the globe, the town of Tampa, Florida, in the United States of America. His lunar space vehicle was shot from a supercharged, nine-foot-caliber cannon, buried in the sands outside that town. His astronaut, Michael Ardan, reached the moon in 97 hours and two minutes. The space capsule on its return trip came to a splash landing in the waters of the Pacific Ocean from which it was safely recovered. These astonishingly accurate predictions of things to come were made nearly 100 years ago — predictions which are strong possibilities today and may well be realities tomorrow.

The Blast-off and the Capsule traveling in Space, from the first American edition of Jules Verne's *From the Earth to the Moon, and a trip Round it*, published by Scribner, Armstrong & Co., New York, 1874

THE MILKY WAY

GALAXY, or VIA LACTEA—the Milky Way, is also called CIRCULUS LACTEUS—the Milky Circle. It is a broad, luminous belt of irregular form entirely surrounding the heavens, and seen only on very dark nights. It has intrigued mankind since earliest times. Explanations for its existence were manifold in bygone days. One of the oldest beliefs was that it was the seam of the two halves of heaven, joined and sewn together with beams of celestial light. In many ancient mythologies it was considered to be the visible path left by deities in their movements —— such as the grain dropped by Isis, the Egyptian goddess of fertility, in her flight from Set, god of evil; the track of the Wild Hunt of Odin, Norse chief god and god of war; the path to the celestial throne of Ormazd, Persian supreme deity and guardian of mankind; and the like. Other mythological beliefs maintained that the Milky Way was a river of celestial light, such as the Arabic

The Greek goddesses of night and day attending to the Milky Way, engraved by Bernhard Maler, from Hyginus' *Poeticon Astronomicon*, printed by Erhard Ratdolt, Venice, 1482

Angels guiding the souls on the celestial highway into Heaven, from
Stephan Lanzkranna's *Das Buch ist genannt Die Hymelstrasz*, printed by
Lucas Zeissemair, Augsburg, 1501

AL-NAHR, or the Chinese TIEN-HO. In ancient Greco-Latin astrology it was already assumed that the Milky Way was a ring of stars, albeit very tiny ones. In Greek legend this circle of stars was made visible and set in motion by Nyx, the goddess of the night, and stopped and hidden by Hemera, the goddess of the day. In early Christian times the Milky Way was called VIA COELI — Heavenly Road, or Highway to Heaven, because it was believed that the souls of the departed were guided by angels over this road to the eternal regions of heaven. This belief that the Milky Way was the path to eternity was not restricted to the early Christians of the Mediterranean region. It was also part of the lore of many primitive peoples in far-flung places from the Pacific Isles to the North American continent, where many American Indian tribes, including the Algonquins and the Iroquois, believed that the Great White Way was the trail on which the

Fanciful picture of a medieval astronomer trying to discover the secrets behind the Milky Way, from an Old German engraving

souls of dead warriors trekked to heaven, and that the bright stars in it were the campfires of these souls resting on their long journey to the Happy Hunting Grounds. The invention of the tele-scope and its adoption in 1609 by Galileo Galilei enabled modern astronomy to confirm the Greek assumption that the Milky Way is a belt of celes-tial bodies. In their research throughout the fol-lowing centuries, astronomers found out that the galaxy is composed of myriads of suns and their satellites, and of nebulae of other galaxies so distant and crowded together that only their united lights could by seen by the unaided eye. Contemporary astronomers are penetrating more and more into the secrets of the Milky Way, and future observers will eventually unveil the last mysteries of our galaxy.

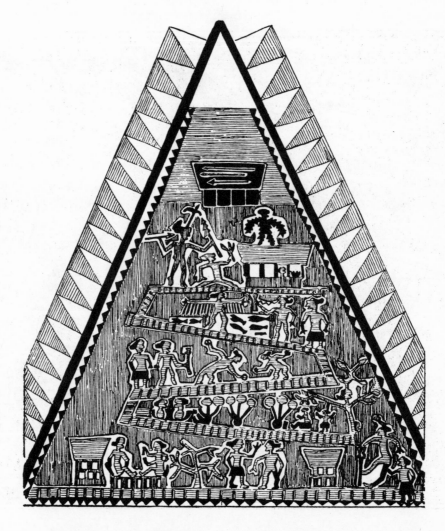

Spirits of slain heroes wandering over the White Way into heaven, from a gable painting in a men's long house, Palau Islands, West Pacific

THE PLANETS

Out of the multitude of heavenly bodies seven were singled out by the ancient astronomers as not conforming to the behavior of the other stars. Almost all the stars seemed to move in concert, maintaining their positions relative to each other. These seven nonconforming celestial bodies, however, moved along their own independent paths among the others, for which performance they were named the PLANETS, derived from the Greek *planetes* — wandering. The seemingly largest two of these bodies were considered the rulers of the sky and the leaders of the stars: the sun as the king of the day, and the moon as the queen of the night. In ancient Chaldea and Babylonia, the cradle of astrology, the worship of the planets as gods was originated. The Greek Pythagoreans in the 5th century B.C., and later on the Romans, adapted this belief for their own use, and substituted their own mythological gods for their Babylonian counterparts:

Emblematic representation of the seven planetary gods, from Johann Daniel Milius' *Philosophia Reformata*, Frankfort/M., 1622

The Seven Planets, from Sebastian Münster's *Organum Uranicum*,
printed by Heinrich Petri, Basle, 1536

for the Babylonian *Adar*, the Greek *Cronus* and and the Roman *Sol* (the sun); for the Babylonian *Sin*, the Greek *Selene* and the Roman *Luna* (the moon); for the Babylonian *Ishtar*, the Greek *Aphrodite* and the Roman *Venus*; for the Babylonian *Nebo*, the Greek *Hermes* and the Roman *Mercury*; for the Babylonian *Nergal*, the Greek *Ares* and the Roman *Mars*; for the Babylonian *Marduk*, the Greek *Zeus* and the Roman *Jupiter*; for the Babylonian *Adar*, the Greek *Cronus* and the Roman *Saturn*. Today we use the Roman designations for the ancient planets. Since the days

Quaint representation of the four elements and the orbits of the planets, from Philippe de Mantegat's *Judicium cum tractibus planetarii*, Milan, 1496

when Nicolaus Copernicus developed his celestial theory and Galileo Galilei confirmed it with his telescopic findings, modern astronomy has greatly changed the ancient concept of the planets. The sun is now the acknowledged center of our celestial system, the earth has been relegated to planetary status, and the moon is known to be the only planet or satellite of the earth. With the development of more powerful telescopes in the centuries following Galileo, new members have been added to the group of solar planets: *Uranus, Neptune,* and *Pluto.* The ancient mythological names of these three modern planets were arbitrarily selected by their discoverers.

The seven planets as the protectors of the farmers, engraved by
V. Feil, from Thannstetter's *Wiener Praktik*, Vienna, 1524

The Planetary Week

The PLANETARY WEEK of Babylonian astronomy, the week of the Greco-Roman planetary gods, the Hebrew-Christian week of the Biblical Genesis, and the Germanic-Anglo-Saxon week of the Nordic gods are the basic ingredients of our week today. The seven planets, which played an important part in Babylonian, Greek and Roman religious life in general, were also believed to influence the seven days of the week through their seven ruling gods. In ancient astrol-ogy, the planet of the day transmitted, under proper conditions, some of the characteristics of its deity to children born under its rays. We still use the Roman names of the influencing gods for the planets themselves, but the names of their days have been superseded by the names of Nordic-Germanic gods, and the significance of these days in our calendar has changed in some cases to that of the Hebrew-Christian seven days of Genesis.

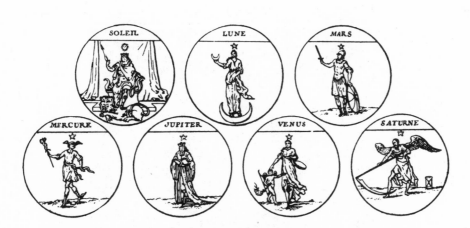

18th-century French planetary talismans for the seven days of the week, from Le Petit Albert's *Secretes merveilleux de la magie*, Cologne, 1722

SUNDAY, from the Anglo-Saxon *sunnan daeg*, translated from the Latin *dies solis* — day of the sun, was considered to be the first day of Genesis in the Old Testament. The Christians changed it to the seventh day of Genesis, and the French still call it *dimanche*, from the Latin *dies dominica* — day of the Lord. It is called in German *Sonntag* — sun's day. In ancient astrology Sunday was considered to be the luckiest day of the week; and the sun bestowed the quality of leadership on a Sunday's child and brought good luck.

MONDAY, in ancient Babylonia, was the day of the week dedicated to the worship of Ishtar, identified with the Phoenician Astarte, goddess of the moon and fertility. Its name is derived from the Anglo-Saxon *monan daeg*, translated from the Latin *lunae dies* — day of Luna, Roman goddess of the moon. The French call it *lundi* — Luna's day, and the Germans *Montag* — day of the moon. The early Christians considered it the first day of Genesis. In ancient astrology a moon's child was dreamy and imaginative.

TUESDAY derives from the Anglo-Saxon *tiwes daeg* — day of Tiw, the Anglo-Saxon god of war, identified with the Nordic war god Tyr, and the Teutonic god of war, Ziu. In ancient Germany it was the day of the week on which the *Thing*, the Germanic court of justice, convened; *Thingstag* — day of the court, was later changed to *Dienstag*. The French call this day *mardi*, from the Latin *martis dies* — day of Mars. In ancient astrology Mars provided children born under his rule with courage and military power.

Title page from a German astrological volume (Here beginneth the book of fortune for the children of Adam), printed by J. Thanner, Leipzig, 1512

WEDNESDAY, in ancient Rome, was the day of the week dedicated to Mercury, god of learning, commerce, travel and the arts. Its English name is derived from the Anglo-Saxon *wodnes daeg* — day of Woden, chief deity of the Germanic tribes. With the advent of Christianity, the heathen day of Woden was changed in Germany simply to *Mittwoch* — middle of the week. The French call it *mercredi*, from the Latin *mercurii dies* — day of Mercury. In ancient astrology a Mercury child had love of learning, travel and art.

THURSDAY in bygone times was dedicated to Jupiter, Roman chief deity, god of lightning and thunder. Its English name is derived from the Anglo-Saxon *thunres daeg* — day of Thor, Anglo-Saxon-Nordic god of thunder. In French it is called *jeudi*, from the Latin *jovis dies* — day of Jove, the poetic name of Jupiter. In German Thursday is called *Donnerstag* — day of Donar, Germanic god of thunder. In ancient astrology Thursday was influenced by the planet Jupiter, who brought good fortune and glory to a child born on his day.

A quaint title page from an Hungarian Gypsy publication (Egypto-Persian Book of Planets), Austria-Hungary, 1890

FRIDAY in antiquity was dedicated to Venus. Its English name is derived from the Anglo-Saxon *frige daeg* — day of Frigg, Nordic goddess of marriage, home and fertility. It is called *vendredi* in French, from the Latin *veneris dies* — day of Venus, Roman goddess of love and beauty. The Germans call it *Freitag* — day of Freya, Germanic deity of love. It was believed in ancient astrology that a child born under the lucky and benevolent rays of the planet Venus would be endowed with beauty and love.

SATURDAY is the Anglo-Saxon *saetern daeg*, translated from the Latin *saturnus dies* — day of Saturn. In French it is called *samedi*, and in German *Samstag*, from the Latin *sabbati dies* — day of Sabbath, derived from the Hebrew *shabath* — to rest. In the Old Testament it was the seventh day of Genesis, on which day the Lord rested. In ancient astrology it was believed to be a most unlucky day, bringing trouble and grief to a child born under Saturn's gloomy rays; a day on which it was wise to avoid decisions.

The Six Days of Creation, from *Biblia Latina*, printed by Lucantonio Giunta, Venice, 1519

THE SUN

Since time immemorial the SUN was venerated as the most exalted star in the heavens. The worship of the sun was widespread throughout antiquity. In nearly every ancient religion of both Occident and Orient, the sun was king of the day, and inevitably represented the supreme creator of nature, dispenser of light, life and power. The Babylonian sun god *Shamash,* carrier of light and life and the symbol of justice, was the Chaldean astrologer's personification of the planet Sun. When the Greeks took their knowledge of astronomy-astrology from the Chaldeans, they assigned the sun to their god *Helios;* and later the Romans identified it with their ancient *Sol.* The Egyptians revered the triple solar deity of *Horus* — the rising sun, *Ra* — the midday sun, and *Atmu* — the setting sun. It was a widespread belief that the sun, like the

Allegoric representation of the sun, *Sol,* engraved by Bernhard Maler, from
Hyginus' *Poeticon Astronomicon,* printed by Erhard Ratdolt, Venice, 1482

Astronomical symbol for the sun — circle and
point, the Orphic egg of creation

Representation of the Persian sun god *Mithras*
as the symbol of light, truth and justice

other planets, traveled over the sky from the east
to the west, only to return through the nether
world to the east again, in some sort of convey-
ance; instances are the solar barge of the Egyptians, the chariot of the Greek Helios, or the cart
of the Roman Sol. At the time of Christ, sun
worship was practiced widely from the Near
East to the Far East. *Mithras,* the Persian god
of the sun, light, truth and justice, was identical
with the Vedic *Mitra,* god of the light of the day.
The Mithraic cult was the most dangerous rival
of Christianity from the time of the Roman
emperor Marcus Ulpius Trajanus (52-117 A.D.),

when Mithraism became the prevailing belief
among the Roman legionaries, until the adoption of the Christian faith by the Roman emperor
Constantine I (273-337 A.D.). Constantine's suc-
cessors ruthlessly destroyed every vestige of the
Mithraic sun worship. In China the sun represented the concrete essence of the masculine
principle; it was the power from which ema-
nated the five colors, the source of all brightness
in life. The ancient Japanese worshiped the sun

The solar barge of the ancient Egyptians, on which the sun travels over
the sky to the west, and returns through the nether world to the east

Symbol of the rising sun, from
an Egyptian hieroglyph

Emblematic representation of the sun as God,
from Boschio's *Arte Symbolica*, Augsburg, 1702

goddess *Ama-terasu* — the Heaven Shining, who was considered to be the ancestress of the emperor of Japan. The sun was also the supreme deity of the Incas and the ancestral god of the Peruvian imperial family. The sun god of the Aztecs was *Tonatiuh*, from the Nahuatl *tona* — he glows. Tonatiuh was worshiped by human sacrifice. Many Indian tribes on the North American continent were sun worshipers, such as the Crow of the plains, the Yuchi and Natchez of the Southeast, the Pueblo and Zuni of the Southwest, and a good number of others. In Western astrology the sun is the luminous heart of the universe, the sign of life and its creative power. It is the symbol of will and wisdom, intelligence and honesty. It is also the emblem of reputation and eminence, honor and glory, dignity and exalted position. It rules Sunday and influences the stomach. Modern astronomy has changed the status of the sun from a mere planet in the ancient terrestrial system to the center star of our solar universe. Today, astronomers consider the sun to be a hot sphere of glowing gases, about

The Aztec sun chief, *Tonatiuh* — the Glowing, who was worshiped
with human sacrifices, from an ancient Mexican stone carving

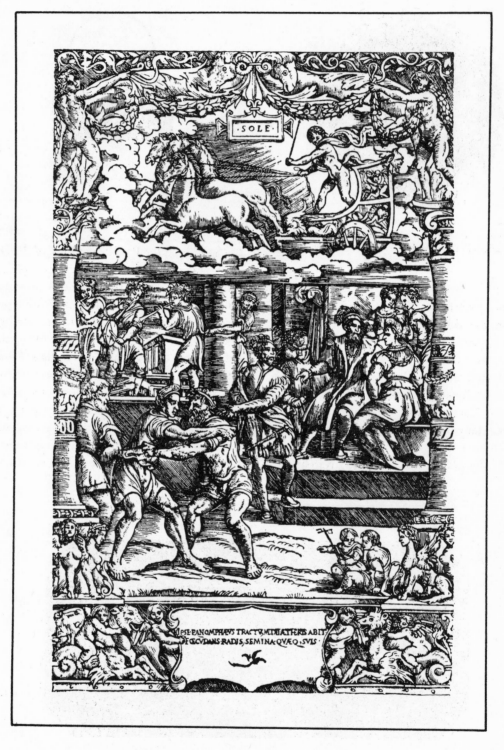

Allegoric representation of the Life of the Children of the Sun,
from an Italian engraving by Gabriele Giolita de Ferrari, 1533

860,000 miles in diameter, with an estimated surface temperature of 11,000 degrees Fahrenheit. Its interior temperature may be as much as 40,000,000 degrees. The mean distance of the sun from the earth is believed to be about 93,000,000 miles. As the astronomical symbol for the sun we still use a point in a circle, the hieroglyphic sign for the Egyptian sun god Ra. In

Colossus Solis of Rhodes, the giant personification of the sun god Helios, engraved by Jean Cousin, from André Thevet's *Cosmographia de Levant,* printed by Jean de Tournes and Guillaume Gazeau, Lyons, 1554

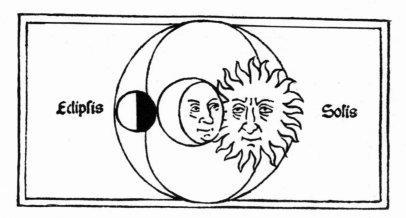

Solar eclipse, from Johannes de Sacrobusco's *Opus Sphaericum*, printed by Erhard Ratdolt, Venice, 1482

remote times it has been the symbol of the universe, the *Orphic Egg*, representing the dot of the sun floating in the ether and enclosed by the vault of the heavens. The English name for the sun is from the Anglo-Saxon *sunne*, derived from the Germanic *Son*, or *Sonne*, which like the French *soleil*, is akin to the Latin *sol*.

Personification of the sun as ruler of the day, from Johannes Winterburger's *Wiener Praktik*, Vienna, 1495

THE MOON

In earliest times the worship of the MOON preceded the worship of the sun. The moon represented the passive or female principle of nature, and its light was believed to be more beneficial to man, beast and the crops than the scorching heat of the sun. The moon was considered the giver of the morning dew, and the source of moisture, the sap of plants, and the blood of man and beast. The moon became the second most important of the ancient Chaldean planets. It was personified by the Babylonian moon god *Sin,* dispeller of darkness and evil, giver of dreams and oracles. The forebodings of the moon were believed to be ambiguous because of its changing phases. Growth was stimulated by its waxing and hindered by its waning. The Greeks changed its personification to *Selene,* goddess of the moon, sister of *Helios* — the Sun, and of *Eos* — the Dawn. In ancient Roman mythology, *Luna,* the goddess of the moon, was iden-

Allegoric representation of the moon, *Luna,* engraved by Bernhard Maler, from Hyginus' *Poeticon Astronomicon,* printed by Erhard Ratdolt, Venice, 1482

Astronomical symbol for the moon, the
crescent of the moon's quarters

The Man in the Moon, from a Venetian
alchemical manuscript, 17th century

tified with the Greek *Selene.* Her name was derived from the Latin *lucere* — to shine. Her worship, which began at the time of Romulus and
Remus (753 B.C.), was later merged with that
of *Diana,* Roman goddess of the moon, the hunt
and virginity, sister of the sun god *Apollo.* The
moon's period coincides with the menstrual period of woman, and has been used as a time
measure of the month. The words *measure,
month, menses* and *moon* grew from the same
root: the Latin *mensus* — to measure. The English name *moon,* from the Anglo-Saxon *mona* —
month, is equivalent to the German *Mond.* The

French still call it *lune,* from the Latin *luna.*
There were many calendars in antiquity that
were based not on the sun but on the moon. Two
of these lunar calendars are still used in our
Western world. The older one is the Hebrew
calendar, Assyrian-Babylonian in origin, reckoning from the year 3761 B.C., the traditional date
of the creation. It is a complicated lunar calendar
with years of 353, 354 and 356 days, and its
months are interspersed with leap months. It

The lunar barge of the ancient Egyptians, on which the moon travels over
the sky to the west, and returns through the nether world to the east

The Moon Rabbit of the Aztecs,
from an ancient Mexican codex

West Indian symbol of the moon,
from an aboriginal rock carving

received its present form from the Jewish patriarch Hillel II (about 360 A.D.). The other lunar calendar is also complicated. It is the Mohammedan, reckoning from the year 622 A.D., traditional date of the *hegira*, the flight of the prophet Mohammed from Mecca. The markings on the face of the moon, seen by the unaided eye, have intrigued man since time immemorial. Many a folk tale was woven around these markings in different lands in all four corners of the globe:

the *Man in the Moon* of Western lore; the *Moon Hare* of India, Tibet, Zululand and ancient Mexico; the Chinese *Three-legged Toad;* the *Hunchback under the Banya Tree* of Malaya; and the *Moon Girl* with a pail under a shrub in the lore of Siberia and some of the northeastern Indian tribes of North America. There are also many tales of frogs, giants, foxes, coyotes and even children. Many a folk tale has set its special brand of inhabitant on the moon as a punishment for a bad deed, or considered it a retreat from persecution or a suitably lonely place to cook up some kind of mischief. In ancient as-

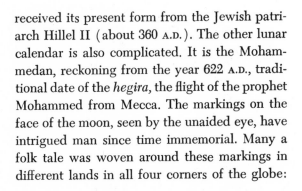

The three-legged Moon Toad, from
an ancient Chinese engraving

The Moon Woman of the Haida
Indians in British Columbia

Luna.

Allegoric representation of the Life of the Children of the Moon, from the
Folge der Planeten, by the German engraver George Pencz (1500-1550)

trology the moon was the star of melancholy, the planet of dreamers and visionaries, the emblem of magnetism, hypnosis, imagination, hallucination, somnambulism and madness. The English term *lunacy* for madness stems from the Latin *luna* — the moon. The moon rules Monday and influences the human brain. The astronomical symbol of the moon is the crescent, the ancient Egyptian emblem of *Isis,* the mother goddess. From the antique concept of a multiple terrestrial planetary system, modern astronomy retains only the twin planetary system of earth and moon. The moon is the only satellite of the earth. It has a diameter of about 2,160 miles, and its distance from the earth is about 238,857 miles. It revolves around the earth in about 27 days, 8 hours. The moon also rotates around its own axis. Its period of rotation is the same as its revolution around the earth, resulting in the fact that one side of it is never seen from the earth. Because of its low surface gravity, the moon probably has no atmosphere, at least none containing oxygen, nitrogen, water vapor, helium or hydrogen. If it has retained any sort

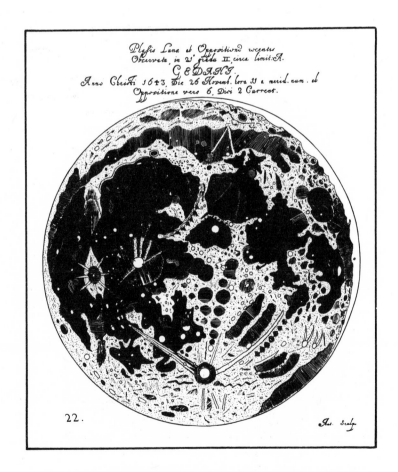

One of the earliest topographic views of the moon, from Johann Hevelius' *Selenographia,* Danzig, 1647

Lunar eclipse, from Johannes de Sacrobusco's *Opus Sphaericum*,
printed by Erhard Ratdolt, Venice, 1482

of atmosphere at all, it can only be one composed of some carbon dioxide and other heavier gases. It is presently believed that the moon is a dead world of frozen lava, its surface pock-marked by craters and criss-crossed by gulches and chasms many hundreds of miles long, a planet which cannot support life in our sense.

The Moon's Phases, designed by Hans Holbein II, from Sebastian Münster's *Canones super novum instrumentum luminarium*, printed by Andreas Cratander, Basel, 1534

MERCURY

MERCURY is the smallest of the ancient Chaldean planets and the nearest to the sun. It was named after the Roman god who presided over commerce and gain, eloquence and manual skill, patron of travelers, heralds, messengers, merchants and thieves. His name, in turn, was derived from the Latin *merx* — merchandise, and he was identified with the Greek *Hermes,* messenger of the gods, deity of science, eloquence and cunning. Hermes himself was the successor of *Nebo* — the Announcer, Assyrian-Babylonian god of wisdom, recorder of the deeds of men, patron of scribes, schools and learning, and the original Chaldean personification of the planet Mercury. In ancient astrology Mercury was the star of intelligence, science, inventiveness, eloquence, and movement as well as mental and physical energy. Mercury rules Wednesday and influences the kidneys in the human body. Its astronomical symbol is a stylized cadu-

Allegoric representation of the planet Mercury, engraved by Bernhard Maler, from Hyginus' *Poeticon Astronomicon,* printed by Erhard Ratdolt, Venice, 1482

Allegoric representation of the Life of the Children of the planet Mercury,
from *Folge der Planeten*, by the German engraver George Pencz (1500-1550)

ceus. In modern astronomy Mercury is a celestial body with a diameter of about 3,100 miles, and its distance from the sun is calculated to be about 36,000,000 miles. It orbits around the sun in about 88 days. It is as bright as a star of the first magnitude, visible to the unaided eye for about two weeks at a time, three times a year. It is best seen as an evening star in the spring

Personification of Mercury, from a broadside by the German
engraver Hans Burgkmair (1473-1531)

Astronomical symbol for the planet Mercury,
the Caduceus of the Roman god of commerce

and as a morning star in the fall. It undergoes phases similar to the moon and has faint permanent markings resembling the canals of Mars.

Since Mercury is so near to the sun, it receives on the side which is permanently turned to the sun ten times as much heat as the earth. The sunny side of the planet Mercury is hot enough to melt lead, and its permanently shady side is so cold that most gases are frozen solid. Because of the low surface gravity of the planet, which cannot hold air, water vapor and light gases, it is believed that the planet Mercury has no atmosphere at all. Mercury seems to be an inhospitable planet with extremely cold and hot hemispheres, a rocky and rugged surface, and a layer of poisonous heavy gases, which will not lend itself to any kind of life as we know it.

Personification of Mercury, the star of science and the arts, from
Nicolas Le Rouge's *Le grant kalendrier des bergieres*, Troyes, 1496

VENUS

VENUS is the third largest of the ancient Chaldean planets. Its original personification was *Ishtar* — the Earth Mother, chief deity of the Assyrian-Babylonian pantheon, goddess of love and marriage. The Phoenicians called her *Astarte*, goddess of sexual love and fertility, similar to the Biblical *Ashtoreth*. The Greeks identified her with their own *Aphrodite*, goddess of beauty, love and marriage, corresponding to the ancient *Venus*, Italian goddess of spring, bloom and beauty. Since the planet was visible before sunrise in the eastern sky as a morning star, the Greeks called it PHOSPHORUS — the Light Bearer, from the Greek *phos* — light, and *pherein* — to bear; the Romans named it LUCIFER — the Light Bringer, from the Latin *lucia* — light, and *ferre* — to bring; and the Hebrews called it HELIEL — the Day Star. As the evening star in

Venus

Allegoric representation of the planet Venus, engraved by Bernhard Maler, from Hyginus' *Poeticon Astronomicon*, printed by Erhard Ratdolt, Venice, 1482

Allegoric representation of the Life of the Children of the planet Venus,
from an Italian engraving by Gabriele Giolita de Ferrari, 1533

the western sky it was named by the Greeks HESPERUS, from the Greek *hesperos* — evening, western. In ancient astrology the brilliant white planet Venus was the star of love and beauty, symbol of gentleness and charm; of taste for music, song and dance; of harmony, playfulness and generosity; and the emblem of love for flowers, jewelry and perfume. Venus rules

Personificaton of Venus, from an engraving by Lucas Cranach the Elder, Wittenberg, 1506

Astronomical symbol for the planet Venus, the
mirror of the Roman goddess of beauty

Friday and influences the kidneys of man. Its
astronomical symbol is a stylized looking glass.
In modern astronomy, Venus is the brightest

object in the sky except for the sun and the moon.
It is the second planet in order of distance from
the sun and the nearest solar planet to the earth.
Its diameter is about 7,700 miles and its distance
from the sun is about 67,180,000 miles. Its period
of revolution around the sun is 224.7 days. It has
a dense atmosphere, with a great abundance of
carbon monoxide as one of its predominant con-
stituents. It has little water vapor and oxygen.
The planet is wrapped in a dense mantle of
clouds, which may be composed mostly of condensed formaldehyde, under which darkness
alternates with foggy days and long twilights.
According to the Venus probe of December,
1962, the planet has a surface temperature of
about 800° F. This precludes the possibility of
life there in any form known to man.

Personification of Venus, star of love, gaiety and music, from Nicolas
Le Rouge's *Le grant kalendrier des bergieres*, Troyes, 1496

MARS

MARS is the fourth largest of the ancient Chaldean planets. Its Assyrian-Babylonian personification was *Nergal,* from *ne-ri-gal* — lord of the nether world, god of war, pestilence and death. The Greeks identified him with *Ares* and the Romans with *Mars,* their own gods of war. In ancient astrology Mars was the blood-red, hostile star of war-making, wrath and brutality, fury and violent sensuality. It was the planet of fire and protector of soldiers; and when it passed nearest to the earth, it unchained wars, revolutions, tempests, earthquakes and other catastrophies. Mars rules Tuesday and influences the human liver. Its astronomical symbol is a stylized shield and spear. In modern astronomy Mars is the fourth planet out from the sun, with a diameter of about 4,200 miles. Its distance from the sun is about 141,500,000 miles and it orbits around the sun in 687 days. Its axis is inclined similarly to that of the earth. Mars has

Allegoric representation of the planet Mars, engraved by Bernhard Maler, from Hyginus' *Poeticon Astronomicon,* printed by Erhard Ratdolt, Venice, 1482

Allegoric representation of the Life of the Children of the planet Mars,
from an Italian engraving by Gabriele Giolita de Ferrari, 1533

atmosphere, seasons, low mountains, clouds and storms. White patches resembling snow and ice cover its poles. Its plains seem to be rocky deserts, and its red color is believed to be the rusty-red of iron ore. Mars has a thin, cold atmosphere which contains some carbon dioxide but only minimal amounts of water vapor and oxygen, permitting only simple forms of plant life, such

Personification of the planet Mars, by Erhard Schön, from a pen drawing at the University Library, Erlangen, Germany, 1540

Astronomical symbol of the planet Mars, the
Roman war god's shield and spear

as algae, mosses and lichens, and highly spe-
cialized organisms of a very low order. There is
a strong possibility that these forms of life exist

on Mars since, as the Martian spring approaches,
parts of the planet's surface change to a green-
brownish color. In 1877, the Italian astronomer
Giovanni Virginio Schiaparelli discovered the
canali, the CANALS OF MARS, which form a
network over the whole planet. The American
astronomer Percival Lowell believed that they
were really canals, which bring water from the
melting polar icecaps to the deserts of the plains;
but nobody really knows what they are. In 1877,
the American astronomer Asaph Hall discovered two minute moons of Mars; he named them
after the two sons of the Greek war god Mars:
the outer one DEIMOS — Terror, and the inner
one PHOBOS — Fear.

Personification of the planet Mars, from *Wiener Praktik*, by
Johann Winterburger, Vienna, 1495

JUPITER

JUPITER is the largest of the ancient Chaldean planets. Its personification was *Marduk* — the Creator, chief god of the Assyrian-Babylonian pantheon, slayer of the watery, primeval serpent-monster of chaos, *Tiamat,* by splitting its body into halves in combat. From one half the earth was formed, and from the other the sky. Armed with the bow of the rainbow and the arrows of lightning, Marduk was the ruler of the universe. The Greeks identified him with their chief god *Zeus,* and the Romans with *Jupiter,* supreme deity of ancient Rome. Presiding over the heavens, Jupiter was considered to be the originator of all changes that took place in the sky, such as rain and hail, lightning and thunder. In ancient astrology Jupiter was the star of good fortune, planet of benevolence and contemplation. It stood between Saturnian slow-

Allegoric representation of the planet Jupiter, engraved by Bernhard Maler, from Hyginus' *Poeticon Astronomicon,* printed by Erhard Ratdolt, Venice, 1482

~ **69**

Allegoric representation of the Life of the Children of the planet Jupiter,
from an Italian engraving by Gabriele Giolita de Ferrari, 1533

ness and Martian haste; the symbol of good will, veneration, spirituality, generosity, nobility and hope. When in the aura of the moon, it bestowed male offspring. Jupiter rules Thursday and influences the human liver. Its astronomical symbol is a stylized bolt of lightning. According to modern astronomy, Jupiter is the nearest and largest of the gaseous giants, with a diameter of about 88,700 miles, 483,000,000 miles from the sun, around which it orbits in 11.86 years. It has a dense, extremely cold atmosphere composed of hydrogen, helium, argon, krypton, pungent ammonia fumes and poisonous methane, but no oxygen. The surface of the planet is obscured by heavy belts of clouds, believed to be crystals of frozen ammonia. If there is any water on Jupiter, it has to be in the form of solid ice. The planet has twelve known satellites, of which the largest

four were discovered in 1610 by Galileo Galilei. They are called the GALILEAN SATELLITES and were named arbitrarily by their discoverer: IO, after the Greek river nymph beloved by Zeus who was changed into a white heifer by the jealous Hera and watched by Argus of the hundred eyes, and who had to escape to Egypt to regain her natural form; EUROPA, after the Phoenician princess who was carried off by Zeus in the form of a white bull and taken across the sea to Crete, where she bore him a son, Minos, king and lawgiver of ancient Crete; GANYMEDE, after the beautiful Greek youth who was taken by Zeus to Mount Olympus, where he became the cupbearer of the gods; and CALLISTO, after the Greek nymph, companion or Artemis, who was seduced by Zeus and bore him a son, Arkas, the mythological ancestor of

Personification of the Assyrian-Babylonian chief god, *Marduk* – the Creator, identified with the Roman Jupiter, from a wall carving in ancient Nineveh

Astronomical symbol for the planet Jupiter, the
lightning bolt of the Roman chief god

the Arcadians. For centuries it was believed that the four Galilean satellites were the only moons of Jupiter, but in the year 1892 the American astronomer Edward Emerson Barnard discovered a small fifth one. And in our century seven more of these diminutive satellites of Jupiter have been identified —— remarkable astronomical achievements, since these satellites are far distant, quite small chunks of rock material only 15 to 100 miles in diameter. The mythological names given by different astronomers to these eight new moons of Jupiter are still not accepted internationally; the satellites are labeled rather by Roman numerals from V to XII in order of their discovery. The Barnard moon is number V; moons number VI and VII were discovered by Jean Baptiste Perrine in 1904 and 1905 respectively; Melotte discovered in 1908 moon number VIII; and the last four were identified by Dr. S. B. Nicholson — number IX in 1914, numbers X and XI in 1938, and the last one, number XII, in 1952.

Fanciful medieval personification of the planet Jupiter,
designed by the Master of the *House-book*, Germany, 1480

SATURN

SATURN is the second largest and most remote of the ancient Chaldean planets. Its personification was the eagle-headed Assyrian hunting god *Nisroch,* identical with the Babylonian *Ninib,* a deity of evil influence who was called the *Great Misfortune.* The Greeks identified him with their Titan *Cronus,* god of harvest and ruler of the universe; and the Romans with *Saturnus,* the ancient Italian god of seedtime and harvest. Cronus was confused with the pre-Hellenic deity of time, *Chronos,* and his astronomical symbol, a stylized sickle of harvest, was erroneously regarded as the sickle of Time. In ancient astrology Saturn was the slow, pale yellow star of mourning and evil courses, the emblem of inertia and death, the symbol of treachery and cowardice. In early Italy it was the star of *jettatore* — thrower of the evil eye. Saturn rules Saturday and influences the lungs. Modern astronomy has calculated that Saturn

Saturnus

Allegoric representation of the planet Saturn, engraved by Bernhard Maler,
from Hyginus' *Poeticon Astronomicon,* printed by Erhard Ratdolt, Venice, 1482

Allegoric representation of the Life of the Children of the planet Saturn,
from *Folge der Planeten*, by the German engraver George Pencz (1500-1550)

has a diameter of about 75,100 miles and that its distance from the sun is about 886,000,000 miles. It has the most extensive high-pressure atmosphere of any planet, extremely cold, containing hydrogen, helium, argon, krypton, poisonous methane and ammonia fumes. The RINGS OF SATURN are a unique occurrence in our solar system. When they were first seen in 1610 by Galileo Galilei through his weak telescope, they looked solid to him, like the handles on a saucer. In 1655 the Dutch natural philosopher Christian Huygens discovered that they had the form of a thin, flat ring, which he believed to be solid or liquid. In 1675 the Italian astronomer Giovanni Dominico Cassini saw a black line separating this ring into two parts, a transparent outer and a bright inner ring. The American astronomer G. Bond discovered in 1850 a third, innermost transparent ring, which he called the CREPE RING OF SATURN. These rings are no longer believed to be solid or liquid, but are now known to be composed of myriads of small celestial bodies orbiting around Saturn in a ring-like formation 10 miles deep and about 171,000 miles in diameter. In 1655 Christian Huygens also discovered the first and largest satellite of Saturn. Since then, eight more have been detected. These nine satellites were arbitrarily named by their discoverers: MIMAS, after the Greek mythological giant who rebelled against the gods and was killed by lightning; ENCELADUS, after the Greek legendary one-hundred-armed giant who warred against the gods, was slain by Athene, and was buried beneath Mount

Personification of the eagle-headed Assyrian hunting god, *Nisroch,* identified with the Roman Saturn, from a wall carving in Nineveh

Astronomical symbol for the planet Saturn, the
sickle of the Greek god Cronus

Etna; THETYS, after the Greek Nereid who was
wooed by both Zeus and Poseidon until an oracle
prophesied that her son would be stronger than
his father —— she married Peleus, king of the
Myrmidons, and bore him a son, Achilles;
DIONE, after the Greek female Titan, mother of
Aphrodite by Zeus; RHEA, after the Greek
mythological wife of Cronus, and mother of
Zeus, Poseidon, Hades, Demeter, Hera and Hes-
tia; TITAN, the largest, brightest and first-dis-
covered satellite of Saturn, after one of the gigantic primeval deities of Greek mythological
legend who were overthrown by their own children, the Olympian gods; HYPERION, after the
Greek Titan, father of the ancient sun god
Helios; JAPETUS, after the Titanic father of
the giant heroes Prometheus, Atlas and Epi-
metheus; and PHOEBE, after the poetic name
of Artemis, Greek goddess of the moon, wild
animals and hunting.

Fanciful medieval personification of the planet Saturn, designed by
the Master of the *House-book*, Germany, 1480

THE EARTH

For ages the EARTH was considered to be the center of the universe. It had many forms and faces in ancient lore and religions. Untold time ago it was believed to be the body of a dead god or a slain monster, or the primeval *materia* born from chaos or rising from the universal waters. At one time or another it was considered to be a flat disk or a square plate floating on the waters of the ocean. Sometimes it was believed to be a cube or a cylinder with a raised rim to hold the waters of the ocean in place; and there were many other forms and shapes ascribed to it. The earth and its atmosphere were composed of four elements — water, fire, air and earth — and a vague fifth element, ether or space. The sky was a vault of solid crystalline matter, studded with lights, resting on the rim of the earth. The earth and the sky

The earth as a disk, from *Etymologarium*, written about 600 A.D. by Isodorus Hispalensis, bishop of Sevilla, printed by Günther Zainer, Augsburg, 1472

Astronomical symbol for the earth,
representing the orb and cross

were sustained by deities, folk heroes, mythological animals, world-trees and other means.
Some examples are the Greek Titan Atlas; the
world-pillars of the Vedic priests; the turtle, elephants and world-serpent of Hindu mythology;
the world-bearing bull of the Asiatic tribes; the
earth toad of ancient Mexico; the world-tree

Yggdrasil of the Norsemen; the world-frogs,
fishes, serpents and cosmic trees of many other
beliefs. In ancient Greece at the time of the epic
poet Homer (9th century B.C.), it was believed
that the earth had the shape of a flat shield,
surrounded by the wide river Oceanus. The
Greek philosopher Thales (640-546 B.C.), the
sage of Miletus in Near Asia, taught the theory
that the earth was a round disk, floating in the
waters of Oceanus, while his contemporary, the
Greek philosopher Anaximander (611-547 B.C.),
considered the earth to be a cylinder. The Greek
philosopher and mathematician Pythagoras
(582-507 B.C.) was the first to believe that the
earth had a spherical form, and that it hung
freely in space, balanced at the center of the
universe. The influential Greek philosopher
Leucippus of Miletus (5th century B.C.) reverted

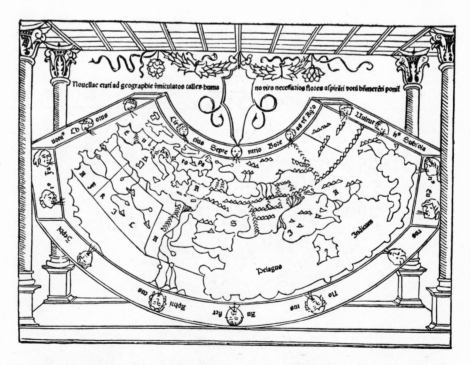

The earth as segment of a disk, from Pomponius Mela's *Cosmographia siva de situ Orbis*,
after Mela's first century A.D. manuscript, printed by Erhard Ratdolt, Venice, 1482

back to the idea of a tympan or kettle drum, with a raised rim holding the waters of Oceanus in place. The Greek philosopher Aristotle (384-322 B.C.) became the greatest expositor of the Pythagorean spherical theory, but the tug of war between the believers in a flat and a spherical earth went on for many centuries. The global form of the earth was not generally accepted

The oldest extant Anglo-Saxon map, showing the square of the earth from the Pillars of Hercules in the west, to Media-India in the east, and from Island (Iceland) in the north to Libia-Ethiopia in the south, 10th century

Pre-Copernican universe, in which the earth was the center, from Cornelius
Cornipolitanus' *Chronographia*, printed by Johann Baruard, Utrecht, 1537

until the circumnavigation of the globe in 1522 by the Portuguese navigator Juan Sebastian del Cano (1460-1526) on the *Victoria*, the last remaining vessel of Magellan's expedition. This established once and for all that the earth is a sphere. The Roman geographer Pomponius Mela (1st century A.D.) still depicted the earth as a flat shield in the form of a disk segment. In the 2nd century A.D., in Alexandria, Egypt, the Greek mathematician and geographer Claudius Ptolemy constructed a mechanistic system of the physical cosmos in which the earth was a sphere, placed in the center of the universe, with the sun, moon and the planets revolving in circles around it. His *celestial sphere* was accepted as correct until the days of the Polish astronomer Nicolaus Copernicus, who theorized that, according to his calculations, the planets

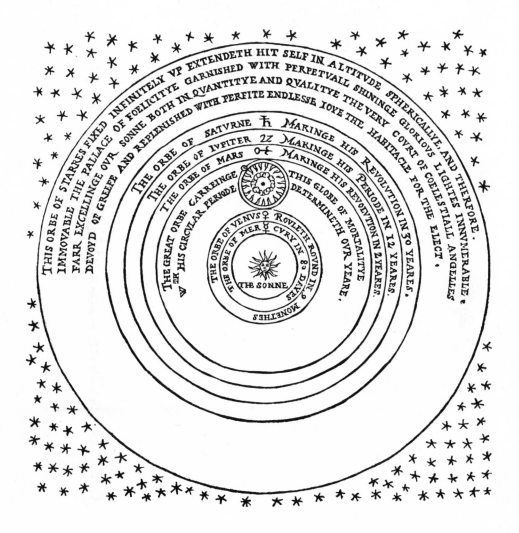

Copernican universe, in which the sun is the center and the moon orbits around the earth, set in an infinite sea of stars, depicted by Thomas Digges, London, 1576

Magellan's ship *Victoria*, skippered by the Portuguese navigator Juan Sebastian del Cano, the first vessel to circumnavigate the globe (1522), from a 16th century engraving

and the earth revolve around the sun, and that the earth also turns on its own axis, thus accounting for the apparent rising and setting of the celestial bodies. This theory is the basic belief of modern astronomy. The Italian astronomer and physicist Galileo Galilei demonstrated the truth of the Copernican system, and with the findings of his telescope relegated the earth to its real position as a small and insignificant member of our planetary system, orbiting with all the other

The Greek Titan *Atlas* supporting the whole universe, from Basile Valentin's *L'Azoth des Philosophes*, Paris, 1659

The world-bearing catfish of Japanese cosmology. Its movements at the ocean bottom under Japan cause the earthquakes

The Aztec symbol of the earth, *Chap-Pek*, the toad, from an ancient
Mexican funeral box for ashes

planets around the sun. He was promptly condemned for heresy by the Inquisition, and had to renounce his discoveries. But as in every other instance in which government has tried to suppress scientific achievements, science prevailed, and modern astronomy was on its way. Modern astronomy has fully vindicated the calculations and findings of Copernicus and Galilei. According to today's scientific knowledge, the earth is the fifth largest planet in our solar system. It is

The Hopi Indian earth-woman, *Hahaiwugti*,
mother goddess of growing, who bore Man,
conceived through the creator-father Sky

Emblematic image of the earth as medium
between light and darkness, from Majer's
Scrutinium Chymicum, Frankfort/M., 1687

a spheroid with an equatorial diameter of 7,927 miles and a polar diameter of 7,900 miles. It is the third planet out from the sun, with an average solar distance of 93,000,000 miles. It orbits around the sun in 365 days, 5 hours, 48 minutes and 46 seconds, or an equinoctial year, and it rotates about its axis, thus causing day and night. Its only satellite is the moon, whose gravitational pull together with that of the sun influences the rise and fall of the tides.

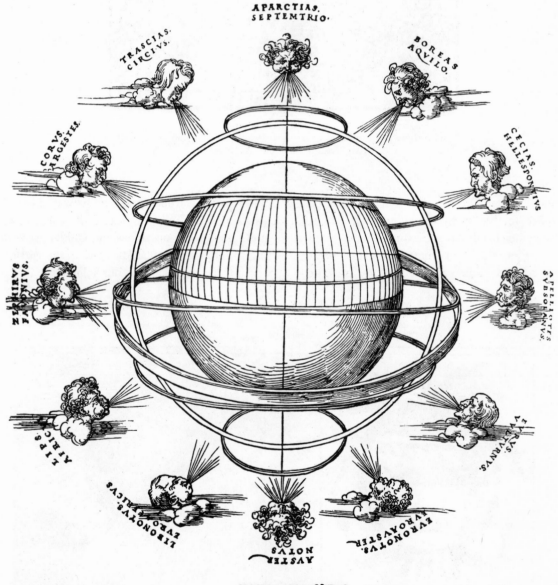

The earth as world center, surrounded by the twelve wind gods, designed by Albrecht Dürer, from Claudius Ptolemy's *Geographicae enarrationes*, printed by Johann Grüninger, Strassburg, 1525

The Modern Planets

Throughout the ages it was assumed that there were only the five planets in our solar system. Not even the extensive use of telescopes by the leading astronomers of the 17th and 18th centuries changed this belief until the year 1781. Then Sir William Herschel discovered a new planet, *Uranus*. Herschel, of a German-Jewish family, was not a learned astronomer, but a musician. He emigrated as a young man to England, where he became music-master at Bath, a watering place in southwestern England. At the age of forty he became fascinated by astronomy and took it up as a hobby, building his own telescopes and scanning the sky in his free time. In 1781 he accidentally discovered the first modern planet, *Uranus*. The second, *Neptune*, was discovered in 1846 by Galle, after its position had been calculated by Leverrier and Adams; and the third, and until today the last, *Pluto*, was found in 1930 by Tombaugh.

URANUS

Astronomical symbol for the planet Uranus, the initial H for Sir William Herschel

URANUS is the first modern planet in our solar system. For a brief period it was called *Herschel*, after the name of its discoverer, Sir William Herschel (1738-1822), and its astronomical symbol is still the initial H. Herschel originally named the planet GEORGIUM SIDUS — Star of George — in honor of George III (1738-1820), king of England. The name was later arbitrarily changed to *Uranus*, for the Greek god of heaven. According to modern astronomical calculations, the planet Uranus has a diameter of about 29,200 miles, and its distance from the sun is about 1,783,000 miles. Its period of revolution around the sun is about 84 of our earth years. Invisible to the unaided eye, it is seen in the telescope as a sea green star. This coloring is caused by the planet's atmosphere, composed almost completely of poisonous methane. Uranus has five satellites: ARIEL, OBERON, TITANIA, UMBRIEL and MIRANDA.

NEPTUNE

Astronomical symbol for the planet Neptune,
the trident of the Roman god of the sea

NEPTUNE is the second modern planet in our universe. It was discovered in 1846 by the German astronomer Johann Gottfried Galle (1812-1910) after its existence had been mathe-matically predicted by Urbain Jean Joseph Leverrier (1811-1877) of France and the English astronomer John Couch Adams (1819-1892). This discovery is regarded as one of the greatest vindications of mathematical astronomy. The planet was named arbitrarily for *Neptune,* Roman god of the sea, and its astronomical symbol is a stylized trident. Neptune has a diameter of about 27,700 miles. Its distance from the sun is about 2,795,000 miles, and its period of revolution around the sun is about 165 earth years. Invisible to the naked eye, Neptune appears in the telescope as a sea green star. This color is caused by a very cold, poisonous atmosphere composed entirely of methane. Neptune has two satellites, TRITON and NEREID.

PLUTO

Astronomical symbol for the planet Pluto, the
monogram PL of the Greek god of Hades

PLUTO is the third and, until today, the last modern planet in our solar system. It was discovered on March 13, 1930 by the American astronomer C. W. Tombaugh of the Lowell Observatory, Flagstaff, Arizona. The discovery was a result of predictions originated in 1905 by the noted American astronomer Dr. Percival Lowell (1855-1916). It was named arbitrarily after *Pluto,* Greek god of the lower world. Its astronomical symbol is the monogram PL. Pluto is the outermost planet in our system, with a diameter of about 8,700 miles, and a distance of about 3,675,000 miles from the sun. Invisible to the unaided eye, it is seen in the telescope as a star of yellow color. To date there is little knowledge about Pluto, and modern astronomy has learned only that the planet is too cold for life to exist there in our sense.

THE ZODIAC

The origins of the ZODIAC — with its concept of the twelve divisions of the year, suggested by the twelve reappearances of the full moon — and of the original twelve animals assigned to the zodiacal constellations, are shrouded in the mist of early history. The Bible called the zodiac simply *Mazzaroth*—the Twelve Signs, in Hebrew. It is very possible that the basic idea of the zodiac was born somewhere in Central Asia, and was accepted about 2700 B.C. by the Assyrian-Babylonian astrologers, who used only eleven of these signs, combining Scorpio and Lyra into one constellation. The Mongolian geomancers of ancient China also used the Central Asian concept for their twelve terrestrial signs. After the conquests of Alexander the Great (356-323 B.C.), the Chaldean astronomers went to Greece and Egypt where they founded schools to teach the accumulated astronomical knowledge of Babylonia as well as

The Zodiac, from *Le grant kalendrier et compost des bergieres,*
printed by Nicolas Le Rouge, Troyes, 1496

their own astrological theories and divinatory practices. Among these were the school of *Alexandria* and the school on the Greek island of *Cos* in the Aegean Sea which was established in 289 B.C. by the Chaldean scientist-priest *Berusus*. The Greco-Roman zodiac was composed first of eleven, and later on of twelve constellations. Its name was derived from the Greek

The Zodiac, from *Le grant kalendrier et compost des bergieres*, printed by Nicolas Le Rouge, Troyes, 1496

The Zodiac, from George Peuerbach's *Tabulae eclipsicum*, printed
by Johannes Winterburger, Vienna, 1514

Armillary sphere with zodiac, from George Peuerbach's *Tabulae
eclipsicum*, printed by Johannes Winterburger, Vienna, 1514

zodiacis — circle of animals. The Chaldean and Greek scholars in the science center of Alexandria forced the Egyptian priests to accept the theory of the twelve zodiacal divisions of the year; and the Egyptian god of learning and magic, *Thoth,* the measurer of time, was designated as the deity of astrological wisdom. The Egyptian zodiac found on the ceiling of the portico in the Temple of Osiris at Denderah, also called the Temple of the Roof, was designed sometime during the rule of the dynasty of the later Ptolemies (before 51 B.C.). The Egyptians changed the Greek designations of some of the zodiacal signs to mythological beings of their own. They substituted for Aries their ram-headed *Amun;* for Taurus, their bull *Apis,* representing Osiris; for Gemini, their gods *Horus the Elder,* and *Horus the Child;* for Cancer, their *Scarabeus;* for Virgo, their goddess *Isis;* and for Aquarius, their water-god *Khum.* The cyclic signs of the *Twelve Terrestrial Branches* of the Chinese zodiac are all animal signs. Its first sign, corresponding with Aries, is *I'zu* — Rat, followed by *Ch-ou*—Ox, *Yin*—Tiger, *Mao*—Hare, *Ch'en*—

Urania holding an armillary sphere with zodiac, from Johannes Stabius'
Prognosticon 1503-1505, designed by Albrecht Dürer, Nuremberg, 1502

Dragon, *Ssu*—Serpent, *Wu*—Horse, *Wei*—Goat, *Shen*—Monkey, *Yu*—Cock, *Hsü*—Dog, and *Hai*—Boar. These twelve zodiacal signs stand for the twelve months of the year. The Japanese copied their zodiac, called *Juni-Shi,* from the Chinese. Their equivalent names for the twelve animals of the months are: *Net*—Rat, *Ushi*—Ox, *Tora*—Tiger, *U*—Hare, *Tatsu*—Dragon, *Mi*—Serpent, *Uma*—Horse, *Hitsu*—Goat, *Saru*—Monkey, *Tori*—Cock, *Inu*—Dog, and *I*—Boar. The zodiac of the twelve animals is known in many lands of the Far East, but there are also other zodiacs used in Far Eastern countries which are combinations of Eastern and Western beliefs. Their signs may have been taken from the conquering peoples of the East—the Mongols, Tatars, Turks, Persians and Arabs. Two of these variations are the Hindu and the Malayan zodiacs, used on the mainland of India and the Malayan Archipelago. The zodiacal signs shown in our reproduction of a Javanese manuscript are: *Mesa*—Ram, *Mirisa*—Bull, *M'rituna*—Butterfly, *Kalakata*—Crab, *Sing-ha*—Lion, *Kanya*—Maiden, *Tula*—Balance, *Mri-chika*—Scorpion, *Danu*—Bow, *Ma*-

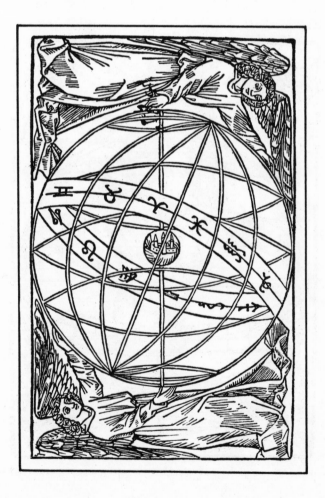

Two antipodal angels holding an armillary sphere with zodiac, from Johann de Sacrobusco's
Textus sphere materialis, printed by Martin Landsperg, Leipzig, 1509

Armillary sphere with zodiac, from Johann de Sacrobusco's *Textus de sphaera*,
printed by Simon Colins, Paris, 1531

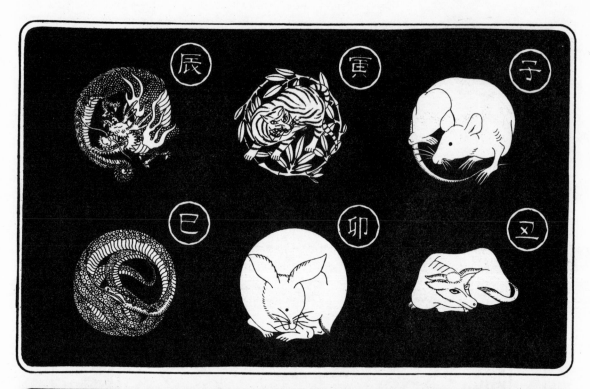

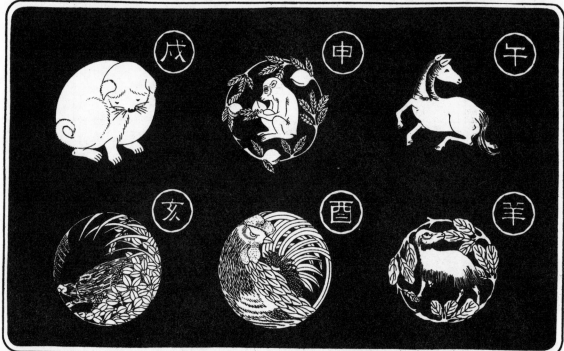

The signs of the Japanese zodiac, from Heishichi Kotany's *Japanese Family Crests*,
Honda Ichijiro, Kyoto, 1915

The signs of the Javanese zodiac, from an ancient Javanese
manuscript, Cheribon, Java

kara—Crawfish, *Kuba*—Water jug, and *Mena*—Fish. The method of reckoning the position of the zodiacal constellations in the ecliptic was devised by the Greek astronomer Hipparchus (190-120 B.C.), who scientifically organized the findings of the Babylonian, Greek and Alexandrian philosophers. He gave the zodiac its astronomical basis, which is still used today. In modern astronomy the zodiac is considered to be an imaginary belt of the celestial sphere extending about 8° on each side of the ecliptic (the apparent path of the sun) and including the orbits of the moon and of all the principal planets. The zodiac is divided into twelve equal parts of 30°, each part named after one of the twelve zodiacal constellations.

Hindu zodiac, with the chariot of the sun in the center, surrounded by eight Hindu constellations, which in turn are enclosed by the twelve zodiacal signs

ARIES

ARIES — The Ram, is the first constellation in the zodiac. The name is derived from the Greek *eras* — lamb. The Chaldean astrologer-priests in their rites for a successful spring sowing, celebrated in the month of March, sacrificed a ram, symbolizing the renewal of the solar energy. The Hebrews, after their exodus from Egypt, also sacrificed the paschal lamb at the Passover festival. This later became the Easter Lamb in Christian. symbology. The Egyptians personified the constellation Aries in their ram-headed *Amun* — the Hidden One, chief god of Libya and Upper Egypt. In Greek legend, Aries was identified with the Golden Fleece, which hung on an oak tree in the sacred grove at Colchis, guarded by a dragon that never slept. The dragon was finally slain by Jason and his Argonauts who took the fleece away. The Arabian astronomers called the constellation HAMAL, from the Arabic *al-hamal* — the sheep.

Aries

Figuration of the zodiacal constellation Aries, engraved by Bernhard Maler, from Hyginus' *Poeticon Astronomicon*, printed by Erhard Ratdolt, Venice, 1482

The astronomical symbol for Aries, a
stylized head and horns of a ram

The constellation Aries, from a
Swiss calendar, 1900

Hamal is used today as the name of the brightest star in Aries. The next brightest star, in the horns of the constellation, is a double star called SHERATAN, from the Arabic *al-sharatan* — the sign. In ancient navigation it was an important stellar landmark used by mariners to determine their longitude at sea, since it is one of the nine bright stars lying along the path of the moon. The third brightest star is also a stellar landmark in the moon's path, a double star named MESARTHIM, from the Hebrew *mesharethim* — the minister. Aries is a northern constellation between Pisces and Taurus, the first spring sign of the zodiac, which the sun enters about the 21st of March. Its astronomical symbol is the stylized head of a ram. In ancient astrology Aries stood for strong will, active intellect, abundant vitality, irritability and violent emotions.

Allegory of March and Aries, from
an English calendar, 1866

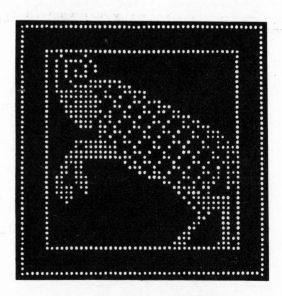

Ornamented representation of Aries,
from a German calendar, 1912

TAURUS

TAURUS — The Bull, is the second constellation in the zodiac. Its name is derived from the Latin *taurus* — bull. In Sumerian-Babylonian legend it was the figuration of a monstrous bull who was created by the sky god *Anu* to give battle to the folk hero Gilgamesh, but was subdued by him. In Greek mythology it represents the white bull transformation of Zeus, in which guise he abducted Europa. The Egyptians named it APIS after the sacred bull of Osiris.

In the Hebrew zodiac it was called ALEPH, from the first letter of the Hebrew alphabet, א, which resembles the triangular face and horns of a bull. The brightest star in Taurus is the brilliant red, first-magnitude ALDEBARAN, from the Arabic *al-dabaran* — the following, because it follows upon the Pleiades; it is also called COR TAURI — Heart of the Bull. The PLEIADES are a star cluster named after the seven daughters of the Titan Atlas and the

Thaurus

Figuration of the zodiacal constellation Taurus, engraved by Bernhard Maler,
from Hyginus' *Poeticon Astronomicon*, printed by Erhard Ratdolt, Venice, 1482

The astronomical symbol for Taurus, a
stylized head and horns of a bull

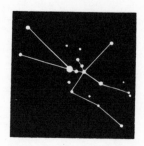

The constellation Taurus, from a
Swiss calendar, 1900

nymph Pleione who, according to the Greek fable, were pursued by Orion, rescued by Zeus, and taken to the sky to become stars. Their names are: ALCYONE, ELECTRA, MAIA, MEROPE, TAYGETA, STEROPE and CE-LAENO. They were called in the Bible CIMAH — the Seven Stars. The HYADES are a V-shaped star group named after seven other daughters of Atlas, nurses of the infant Zeus, who were also changed into stars. The Hyades and Alde-baran are part of a star group called the TAURUS CLUSTER. The second brightest star in Taurus is EL-NATH, from the Arabic *al-nath* — the goring. Taurus contains the CRAB NEBULA, the remnant of a *supernova* recorded in 1054 by Chinese astronomers. This northern constellation between Aries and Gemini is the second spring sign in the zodiac, which the sun enters about the 20th of April. Its astronomical symbol is the stylized head of a bull. In ancient astrology Taurus stood for boldness, strength, courage and leadership.

Allegory of April and Taurus, from
an English calendar, 1866

Ornamented representation of Taurus,
from a German calendar, 1912

GEMINI

GEMINI — The Twins, is the third constellation in the zodiac. Its two brightest stars, CASTOR and POLLUX, have been regarded as a pair since earliest times, as long ago as 6,000 B.C., in Mesopotamia. In ancient Hebrew astrology they were considered to be the two pillars which Solomon raised outside of the temple in Jerusalem. These pillars were called JACHIN BOAZ, from the Hebrew *jachin* — He will establish, and *boaz* — in Him is strength. Greek astronomers changed the meaning of this constellation to the representation of *Castor* and *Pollux,* twin sons of Zeus. Castor was mortal and Pollux immortal. When Castor was slain in a brawl, the grieving Pollux implored his father to let him die, too. Zeus granted his wish and moved the twins into heaven. The constellation became known as the DIOSCURI, from the Greek *dios* — god, and *kuroi* — sons; the Romans changed the name to *gemini,* Latin for twins. The Egyptians regarded

Personification of the zodiacal constellation Gemini, engraved by Bernhard Maler, from Hyginus' *Poeticon Astronomicon*, printed by Erhard Ratdolt, Venice, 1482

Astronomical symbol for Gemini, stylized
columns of Solomon's temple

The constellation Gemini, from a
Swiss calendar, 1900

these two stars as *Horus the Elder* and *Horus the Child;* their hieroglyphic symbol for the constellation was two sprouting plants, because fresh sprouts were springing up when the sun was in the sign of the two Horuses. The Arabians called them the *Two Peacocks;* the Hindus named them the *Two Horsemen;* and the Chinese recognized them as the representation of the male-female principle, *Yang and Yin.* Castor and Pollux are first-magnitude stars. Both seem to be multiple star systems, with each having probably six components. Gemini is a northern constellation between Taurus and Cancer, the third spring sign in the zodiac, which the sun enters about the 21st of May. Its astronomical symbol is the stylized twin pillars of Solomon's temple. In ancient astrology Gemini stood for affection, filial love, devotion, friendship, initiative, selflessness and love of the sciences and arts.

Allegory of May and Gemini, from
an English calendar, 1866

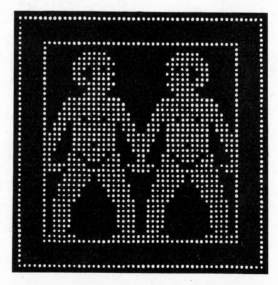

Ornamented representation of Gemini,
from a German calendar, 1912

CANCER

CANCER — The Crab, is the fourth constellation in the zodiac. Its name is derived from the Latin *cancer* — crab. In Greek legend it is the reincarnation of the giant crab which Juno, offended by Heracles, sent to punish the hero who was fighting the nine-headed Hydra. But the injured Heracles stepped on the crab and crushed it. Juno, out of gratitude for its services, placed it among the stars. The Egyptians called the constellation SCARAB, symbol of their sun god *Khepera*, the creator of life, whose name was derived from the Egyptian *kheper* — turning back (like a crab). In ancient Chaldean belief Cancer was the *Gate of Men*, through which the souls of the newborn entered the earth. The brightest star in Cancer is the double star ACUBENS, from the Arabic *al-zubayan* — the two claws; its second brightest is AL TARF, from the Arabic *al-tarf* — the end. An open star cluster composed of about 500 bright stars is

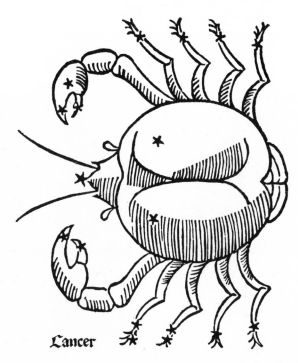

Lancer

Figuration of the zodiacal constellation Cancer, engraved by Bernhard Maler, from Hyginus' *Poeticon Astronomicon*, printed by Erhard Ratdolt, Venice, 1482

Astronomical symbol for Cancer, the
stylized folded claws of a crab

The constellation Cancer, from a
Swiss calendar, 1900

named PRAESEPE, from the Latin *praesaepe* —
manger; it is also called the BEEHIVE. It is
flanked by the third and fourth brightest stars
in Cancer, ASELLUS BOREALIS and ASEL-
LUS AUSTRALIS, from the Latin *asellus*—little
ass, *borealis*—northern, and *australis*—southern.
According to Greek lore, two asses, aiding the
gods in their fight with the Titans, entered the
battle braying so loudly that they terrified the
giants, who fled. The thankful gods placed the
two little asses among the stars, and put between them *Praesepe* — the manger, where they
could constantly feed. This northern constellation in the zodiac between Gemini and Leo is
the first summer sign, which the sun enters about
the 21st of June. Its astronomical symbol is two
stylized claws of a crab. In ancient astrology
Cancer stood for romantic impressionability,
paradoxical presumption and mediocrity.

Allegory of June and Cancer, from
an English calendar, 1866

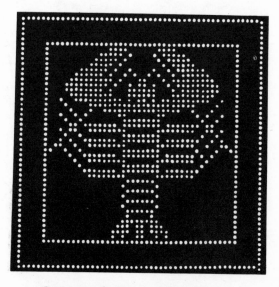

Ornamented representation of Cancer,
from a German calendar, 1912

LEO

LEO — the Lion, is the fifth constellation of the zodiac. Its name is derived from the Latin *leo* — lion. Since 4000 B.C. it has always been considered as a lion everywhere, ruler of all constellations, symbolizing the heat and creative energy of the summer sun. The brightest star in Leo is the first magnitude REGULUS, from the Latin *regulus* — little king. This name was given to the star by Nicolaus Copernicus, who changed it from the ancient name BASILICOS (Greek *basilikos* — royal) which had been bestowed upon the star by Claudius Ptolemy, whose entire conception of the universe Copernicus had overthrown. The star was also known as COR LEONIS — the Heart of the Lion. Lying along the path of the moon, it was one of the nine lunar stars that were used by mariners in taking their longitude at sea. The second brightest star in the constellation is DENEBOLA, from the Arabic *dhanab al-asad* — tail of the lion, a star

Figuration of the zodiacal constellation Leo, engraved by Bernhard Maler, from Hyginus' *Poeticon Astronomicon*, printed by Erhard Ratdolt, Venice, 1482

Astronomical symbol for Leo, a
stylized sun with lion's tail

The constellation Leo, from a
Swiss calendar, 1900

which was considered by astrologers as unlucky, tending to misfortune and public disgrace; it is one of the four stars forming the GREAT DIA-MOND OF VIRGO. The third brightest star in Leo is ALGIEBA, from the arabic *al-jabhah* — the forehead. The constellation Leo also contains a stellar landmark, the SICKLE OF LEO, a sickle-shaped formation of six stars, with Regulus forming the handle. Leo is a northern constel-lation between Cancer and Virgo, the second summer sign of the zodiac, which the sun enters about the 22nd of July. Its astronomical symbol is a stylized sun with the tail of a lion, derived from a phallic emblem of ancient Dionysian mysteries. In ancient astrology Leo stood for royal power and virtue, nobility of character and manly courage, generosity and prudence, firm-ness, calmness and physical strength.

Allegory of July and Leo, from an
English calendar, 1866

Ornamented representation of Leo,
from a German calendar, 1912

VIRGO

VIRGO — the Virgin, is the sixth constellation in the zodiac. The name is derived from the Latin *virginis* — maiden. The Assyrian-Babylonian astronomers called it BELIT, after the consort of their chief god, Bel; the Phoenicians named it PARA-ISIS — the Star of Being. Since earliest times Virgo has been identified with goddesses of the harvest — in Egypt with Isis, in Greece with Ceres, in Rome with Demeter — and the Arabians called it EL SUMBELA, from the Arabic *al-zumbelah* — the ear of grain. In ancient star maps the constellation was personified by a maiden holding a branch or a spike of grain. Its brightest star is the first-magnitude SPICA, from the Latin *spica* — ear of grain, and its second brightest ZAVIJAVA, from the Arabic *al-zawiyah* — the angle. The third brightest star in Virgo is a double star named PORRINA, after an ancient Latin goddess of prophesy. The fourth brightest star is called VINDEMIATRIX, the

Uirgo

Personification of the zodiacal constellation Virgo, engraved by Bernhard Maler, from Hyginus' *Poeticon Astronomicon*, printed by Erhard Ratdolt, Venice, 1482

Astronomical symbol for Virgo, the
stylized girdle of Hymen

The constellation Virgo, from a
Swiss calendar, 1900

Latin word for female grape-gatherer. The constellation contains the VIRGO CLUSTER, the brightest, largest and nearest of the great clusters in our universe. It is composed of several hundreds of bright external galaxies. A stellar landmark in the northern hemisphere in the form of a great diamond, called the DIAMOND OF VIRGO, is shaped by four bright stars: Spica in the constellation Virgo; Cor Caroli in Canes Venatici; Arcturus in Boötes; and Denebola in the constellation Leo. Virgo is a northern constellation between Leo and Libra, the third summer sign in the zodiac, which the sun enters about the 23rd of August. Its astronomical symbol is the stylized girdle of Hymen. In ancient astrology the constellation Virgo was considered to be the ruler of the womb, standing for all virtues: sympathy, prudence, tact, ability, ingenuity, taste for art, and love of the rare and beautiful.

Allegory of August and Virgo, from
an English calendar, 1866

Ornamented representation of Virgo,
from a German calendar, 1912

LIBRA

LIBRA — the Balance, is the seventh constellation in the zodiac. The name is derived from the Latin *libra* — balance. In ancient writings it was called TUL KU — the Holy Altar, and, according to the Bible, the altars in both the first and the second temples were dedicated to the seventh month, the month of Libra. The early Greeks combined the stars of the Altar with those of Scorpio, designating them as the claws of the scorpion. Libra is the only sign in our zodiac which is not of Euphratean origin. We owe the declaration of Libra as a separate constellation to the Romans. When Julius Caesar called Alexandrian astronomers to Rome to calculate the Julian Calendar, the astronomers changed the Altar in their star maps to the figure of Caesar holding a scale and dispensing justice. After the death of Caesar, his figuration was dropped

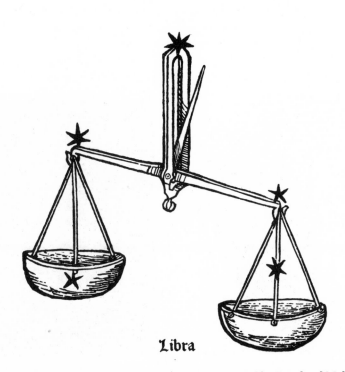

Libra

Figuration of the zodiacal constellation Libra, engraved by Bernhard Maler, from Hyginus' *Poeticon Astronomicon*, printed by Erhard Ratdolt, Venice, 1482

Astronomical symbol for Libra,
a stylized pair of scales

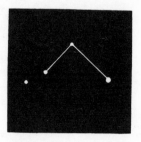

The constellation Libra, from a
Swiss calendar, 1900

from the maps and only the balance, Libra, re-mained. The Egyptians considered Libra to be the yoke of the water-balance with which the rising and falling of the Nile level was measured. The brightest star in Libra is the yellow-gray double star KIFFA AUSTRALIS, from the Arabic *quffah* — basket, and the Latin *australis* — southern, also called the SOUTHERN CLAW (of Scorpio), a star of evil reputation in astrology. The second brightest star is the green-colored KIFFA BOREALIS, from the Latin *bo-*

realis — northern, also called the NORTHERN CLAW (of Scorpio), and highly regarded by ancient astrologers as a star of especially good fortune. Libra is a southern constellation between Virgo and Scorpio, the first autumn sign in the zodiac, which the sun enters about the 23rd of September. Its astronomical symbol is a stylized balance. In ancient astrology Libra was considered the constellation of equilibrium and justice, standing for equity, connections, contacts, artistry and amorous passion.

Allegory of September and Libra, from
an English calendar, 1866

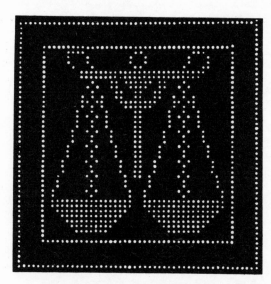

Ornamented representation of Libra,
from a German calendar, 1912

SCORPIO

SCORPIO — the Scorpion, is the eighth constellation in the zodiac. (In modern astronomy the star group is known as SCORPIUS.) Its name is derived from the Greek *skorpios* — scorpion. The Akkadians called it GIRTAB — the Stinger, and the Hebrews AKRABH — the Scorpion. In Greek classical legend it was the stellar reincarnation of the monstrous scorpion that killed Orion, the Giant Hunter, after he boasted to Diana that there was no creature on earth he could not subdue. Orion still flees before the scorpion; as Scorpio rises, Orion sets. In ancient times Scorpio included the stars of Libra which shaped the claws of Scorpio. The Egyptians considered the constellation the stellar representation of SELK, goddess of the scorching heat of the sun, depicted as a monster with the head, bust and arms of a woman, and the tail and sting of a scorpion. The brightest star in Scorpio is the first-magnitude ANTARES, from the Greek *anti*

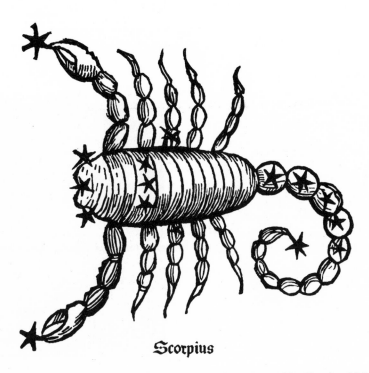

Scorpius

Figuration of the zodiacal constellation Scorpio, engraved by Bernhard Maler, from Hyginus' *Poeticon Astronomicon*, printed by Erhard Ratdolt, Venice, 1482

Astronomical symbol for Scorpio, a
stylized arrow-tailed serpent

The constellation Scorpio, from
a Swiss calendar, 1900

— rivaling, and *Ares* — Mars, because its red color is like the color of the planet Mars. It is a giant star of low density, believed to be the fourth largest in heaven, with a diameter of about 415,000,000 miles; it is also called COR SCORPII — the Heart of the Scorpion. The second brightest star in the constellation is the white-lilac double star ACRAB, from the Arabic *al-agrab* — the scorpion, and the third brightest SHAULA, from the Arabic *al-shawlah* — the sting. A beautiful quadruple star, the fourth brightest in Scorpio, is DSCHUBBA, from the Arabic *al-jabbah* — the forehead. Scorpio is a southern constellation between Libra and Sagittarius, the second autumn sign of the zodiac, which the sun enters about the 23rd of October. Its astronomical symbol is a stylized serpent with an arrow-tail. In ancient astrology it was an ill-omened constellation, bringing in its wake, darkness, storms, duels, fights and accidents.

Allegory of October and Scorpio, from
an English calendar, 1866

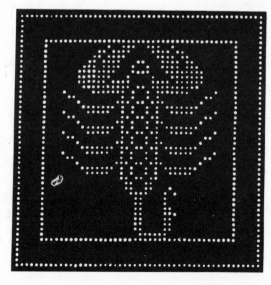

Ornamented representation of Scorpio,
from a German calendar, 1912

SAGITTARIUS

SAGITTARIUS — the Archer, is the ninth constellation in the zodiac. Its name is derived from the Latin *sagittarius* — of an arrow, the archer. From earliest times the constellation was symbolized by a bow and arrow. The Hebrews called it KESHET; the Persians, KAMAN; the Turks, YAI, and the Arabs, EL KAUS—all meaning a bow. In Greek mythological lore it represented the wild, arrow-shooting Centaur, the son of Ixion, king of Lapithae, and a phantom cloud resembling Hera which Zeus substituted for the queen of the gods when Ixion was about to rape her. The brightest star in Sagittarius is RUKBAT, from the Arabic *rukba al-rami* — knee of the archer, and the second brightest is a double star URKAB, from the Arabic *al-urqub* — the tendon. The next three brightest stars in the constellation, forming the bow of the archer, are KAUS BOREALIS, KAUS MEDIA and KAUS AUSTRALIS, from the Arabic *qaws* — bow, and the

Figuration of the zodiacal constellation Sagittarius, engraved by Bernhard Maler, from Hyginus' *Poeticon Astronomicon*, printed by Erhard Ratdolt, Venice, 1482

Astronomical symbol for Sagittarius, a
stylized representation of an arrow

The constellation Sagittarius, from
a Swiss calendar, 1900

Latin *borealis* — northern, *media* — middle, and *australis* — southern. Sagittarius is situated in one of the richest sections of the Milky Way. Here are found the OMEGA NEBULA, a diffuse nebula in the form of the Greek letter Ω, also called the HORSESHOE NEBULA; the LAGOON NEBULA, from the Latin *lacuna* — pond, a star cluster nebula in the form of an atoll; the TRIFID NEBULA, from the Latin *tri* — three, and *findere* — to split, a large, gaseous nebula divided by dark lanes into three principal masses; and the SAGITTARIUS STAR CLOUD, the largest and most magnificent cluster in the Milky Way. Sagittarius is a southern constellation between Scorpio and Capricorn, the third autumn sign, which the Sun enters about the 23rd of November. Its astronomical symbol is a stylized arrow. According to ancient astrology, Sagittarius stood for energy, love of hunting, effort and aiming at the stars.

Allegory of November and Sagittarius,
from an English calendar, 1866

Ornamented representation of Sagittarius,
from a German calendar, 1912

CAPRICORN

CAPRICORN — the Goat, is the tenth constellation in the zodiac. Its name is derived from the Latin *caper* – goat, and *cornu* — horn. Since earliest times it was depicted in zodiacal charts as a horned goat, or ibex. The Chaldean astronomers believed that this constellation was the entrance through which the souls of the dead passed into heaven, and so it was called the GATE OF GODS. In Greek legend, it was the stellar reincarnation of the goat-footed, hoofed *Pan*, god of the fields and flocks, who, pursued and attacked on the banks of the Nile by the monster Typhon, plunged into the river, changing himself into a monster-goat with the hind quarters of a fish. The brightest star in Capricorn is the double star ALGIEDI, from the Arabic *al-jadi* — the kid, and the second brightest DAHIB, from the Aribic *al sa'd al-dhahib*—the lucky one of the slaughterers, referring to the sacrifice of a goat, celebrated by the Arabs on the heliacal

Figuration of the zodiacal constellation Capricorn, engraved by Bernhard Maler,
from Hyginus' *Poeticon Astronomicon*, printed by Erhard Ratdolt, Venice, 1482

Astronomical symbol for Capricorn, a
stylized goat with fishtail

The constellation Capricorn, from
a Swiss calendar, 1900

rising of Capricorn. The third brightest star in the constellation is NASHIRA, from the Arabic *al-nashirah* — the announcer of good tidings; and the fourth-brightest DENEB ALGIEDI, from the Arabic *dhanab al-jadi* — tail of the kid. A stellar landmark formed by the three stars Algiedi, Dahib and Deneb Algiedi in the form of a yoke, is called the YOKE, from the Latin *jugere* — to join. In the year 1846 the planet Nep-

tune was discovered among the stars of the constellation Capricorn. Capricorn is a southern constellation between Sagittarius and Aquarius, the first winter sign of the zodiac, which the sun enters about the 21st of December. Its astronomical symbol is a stylized rearing goat with a fishtail. In ancient astrology the constellation Capricorn stood for mournfulness, impassivity, inconstancy and egotism.

Allegory of December and Capricorn,
from an English calendar, 1866

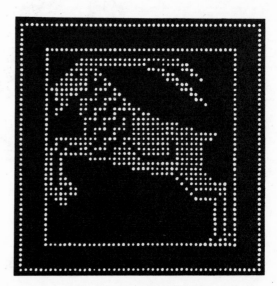

Ornamented representation of Capricorn,
from a German calendar, 1912

AQUARIUS

AQUARIUS — the Water Bearer, is the eleventh constellation in the zodiac. Its name is derived from the Latin *aquarius* — of water, or water pitcher. In early times the constellation was symbolized everywhere as a water pitcher. In ancient Babylonia it was GU — the Water Jar, and to the Akkadians KU UR KU — Seat of the Flowing Waters. The Hebrews, Syrians, Persians, Turks and Hindus all regarded it as a water bucket. The Greeks added the figure of a man, and identified the constellation with *Ganymede*, the cupbearer of the gods. The Egyptians equated it with *Khum*, the god of the life-giving water. The brightest star in Aquarius is a pale-yellow and gray double star, SADALMALIK, from the Arabic *sa'd al-malik* — the good luck of the king; the second brightest star is the pale-yellow SADALSUUD, from the Arabic *sa'd al-suud* — the luckiest of good lucks, because it rises with the sun when the cold days of winter

Aquarius

Personification of the zodiacal constellation Aquarius, engraved by Bernhard Maler, from Hyginus' *Poeticon Astronomicon*, printed by Erhard Ratdolt, Venice, 1482

Astronomical symbol for Aquarius,
a stylized double wave of water

The constellation Aquarius, from
a Swiss calendar, 1900

have passed. The ancient astrologers called it FORTUNA FORTUNATUM, the fortune of good luck. The third brightest star in the constellation is the green-colored SADACHBIA, from the Arabic *sa'd al-akhbiyah* — the good luck of the tent, considered to be the lucky star of all hidden things because when it rose with the sun all the little creatures came out of their burrows into the warm sunshine. Aquarius contains the SATURN NEBULA, a small nebula whose shape resembles the globe and rings of the planet Saturn. Aquarius is a southern constellation between Capricorn and Pisces, the second winter sign of the zodiac, which the Sun enters about the 20th of January. Its astronomical symbol is a stylized double wave of water. In ancient astrology Aquarius was the constellation which stood for discretion, fidelity, thoughtfulness, love of fine arts, benevolence, mysticism and submission.

Allegory of January and Aquarius, from
an English calendar, 1866

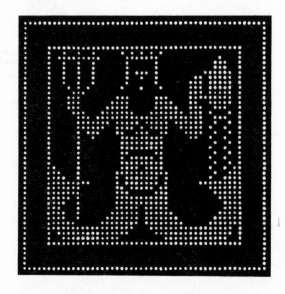

Ornamented representation of Aquarius,
from a German calendar, 1912

PISCES

PISCES — the Fishes, is the twelfth constellation in the zodiac. It is composed of two widely separated star groups joined together by a ribbon of stars, and its name is derived from the plural of the Latin *piscis* — fish. The Assyrian-Babylonians called it NANU — the Fish, and the Philistine-Phoenicians named it after their fish-tailed chief deity, *Dagon*, god of agriculture, who was mentioned many times in the Old Testament. Greek mythological lore believed that the Pisces were the stellar reincarnations of the two dolphins who carried the chariot of shells in which the wife of Poseidon, Amphitrite, queen of the sea, rode through the waves. In Roman legend Pisces represented the two fishes into which Venus and Amor transformed themselves as they fled through the river Euphrates from Typhon, the monster with the hundred dragon-heads who

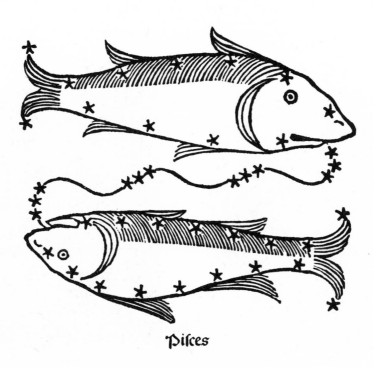

Pisces

Figuration of the zodiacal constellation Pisces, engraved by Bernhard Maler,
from Hyginus' *Poeticon Astronomicon*, printed by Erhard Ratdolt, Venice, 1482

Astronomical symbol for Pisces,
a stylized yoke of dolphins

The constellation Pisces, from
a Swiss calendar, 1900

tried to destroy them. The Romans called the constellation VENUS CUM CUPID — Venus and Cupid. The Arabs named it HUT — the Fish, and its brightest star AL RISHA, from the Arabic *al-risha* — the cord or ribbon. In medieval times, Christian astronomers identified Pisces with the Biblical fish which Jesus fed to the multitude. In the year 6 B.C., an astronomical triple conjunction occurred between the star Al Risha and the planets Mars, Jupiter and Saturn. This brilliant phenomenon in the sky may possibly have been the origin of the Biblical story of the STAR OF BETHLEHEM. Pisces is a southern constellation between Aquarius and Aries, the third winter sign of the zodiac, which the sun enters about the 18th of February. Its astronomical symbol is a pair of dolphins yoked together. It was considered by ancient mariners to be a rainy constellation, bringing storms and disaster. In ancient astrology it stood for indolence, timidity, hypocrisy and slander.

Allegory of February and Pisces,
from an English calendar, 1866

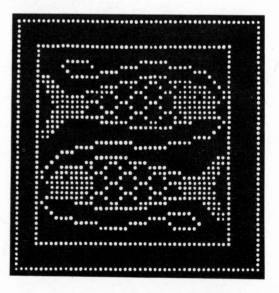

Ornamented representation of Pisces,
from a German calendar, 1912

The Celestial Sphere

Astronomers of bygone days considered the heavens to be a vault or sphere studded with stars. Besides the *wandering* stars, or planets, there were others which supposedly did not change their positions relative to one another, and for that reason were called *fixed* stars. This denotation is in reality a misnomer, because these so-called fixed stars do change their positions, but so slowly and over such a long period of time that the fact escaped the observation of the ancient astronomers. These fixed stars, organized by the old philosophers into arbitrary groups with imaginary outlines, are also called CONSTELLATIONS, from the Latin *com* — together, and *stellar* — to shine. Each of these constellations was named after some mythical god, hero, animal or inanimate object, whose image or configuration had a fancied correspondence to the outline of the star group. Notwithstanding the fact that the Babylonian astronomers had al-

Arabian astronomer constructing a celestial globe, from Alboul Hassan Ali's *Praeclarissimus in Juditijs Astrorum*, Venice, 1519

ready developed an extensive descriptive knowledge of the celestial phenomena, the Greek philosophers reconstructed and renamed the constellations after their own mythological be-

liefs. The Egyptians, Romans, and later the Arabs took their celestial sphere from the Greeks, changing some of the names and mythological meanings to suit their own beliefs. The medieval

The Southern Hemisphere of the Celestial Globe, designed by the
Arabic astronomer Mohammud ben Helah of Monsul, 1275

astronomers of the Western world acquired the design of their celestial globe from the Arabs, and the names of their constellations from the Romans. The celestial globe of the Far East is completely different from the Western concept. The Chinese philosophers developed their own idea of a celestial sphere and their conception became the basis of many a Far Eastern globe.

The Northern Hemisphere of the Celestial Globe, designed by the
Arabic astronomer Mohammud ben Helah of Monsul, 1275

According to ancient Chinese belief, the central earth is surrounded by the *Four Supernatural Creatures,* presiding over the *Four Quadrants of* *Heaven*: the *Azure Dragon* over the East; the *Vermillion Bird,* or Phoenix, over the South; the *White Tiger* over the West; and the *Black War-*

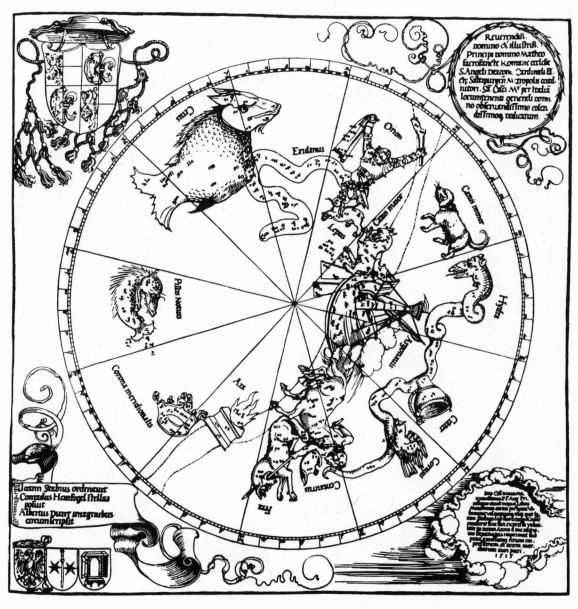

The Southern Hemisphere of the Celestial Globe, designed by Albrecht Dürer
for Johannes Stabius, Vienna, 1515

rior, or Tortoise, over the North. These four quadrants are enclosed by the *Pa Kua,* or Eight Diagrams, representing heaven, water, lightning, thunder, wind, clouds, mountains and earth. They are encircled by the twelve zodiacal animals, which in turn are surrounded by the 28

The Northern Hemisphere of the Celestial Globe, designed by Albrecht Dürer
for Johannes Stabius, Vienna, 1515

Kung, or constellations of the Chinese heaven: the Earth Dragon, the Sky Dragon, the Badger, the Hare, the Fox, the Tiger, the Leopard, the Griffon, the Ox, the Bat, the Rat, the Swallow, the Bear, the Porcupine, the Wolf, the Dog, the Pheasant, the Cock, the Raven, the Monkey, the Ape, the Tapir, the Sheep, the Muntjak, the Horse, the Deer, the Snake and the Worm. In our own celestial sphere today, we still use the Greek and Roman designations for the ancient

The Egyptian celestial sphere from the Temple of Osiris at Denderah, designed in the time of the later Ptolemies, between 305 and 51 B.C.

constellations, but most of the names that we use for the individual stars of which these constellations are composed are the designations given to them by the Arabic astronomers. The invention of the telescope in the early 17th century made possible the discovery of more and more star groups not seen by the unaided eyes of the ancient observers, and modern astronomers have found and named many new constellations.

The Chinese celestial sphere, engraved on a brass mirror of the
T'ang Period, China, 618-905 A.D.

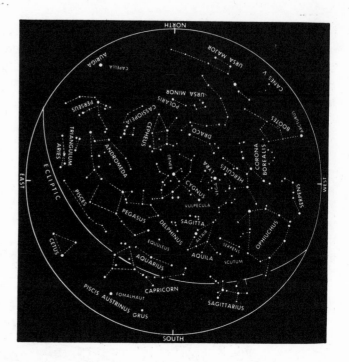

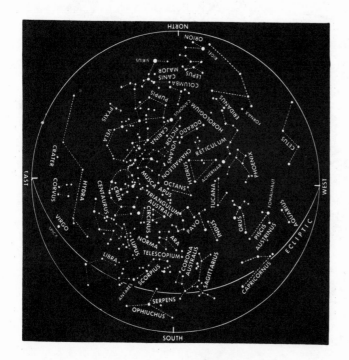

The northern and southern hemispheres of the celestial globe
in modern representation

The Ancient Constellations

ANDROMEDA — the Chained Lady, is a northern constellation between Pegasus and Perseus. In Greek mythological legend she was the daughter of Cepheus and Cassiopeia, king and queen of Ethiopia, and wife of Perseus. Because her mother bragged that Andromeda was more beautiful than the Nereids, Poseidon sent floods and the sea monster Cetus to destroy Ethiopia. The oracle of Zeus-Ammon decreed that the land could be saved from destruction only if Andromeda were chained to a cliff to be devoured by Cetus. Perseus, returning on Pegasus from the slaying of Medusa, saw the chained maiden attacked by Cetus. Engaging the monster in combat, he held Medusa's head before it. Cetus was turned into stone; and Perseus married the princess. The brightest star in Andromeda is ALPHERATZ, from the Arabic *al-faras*

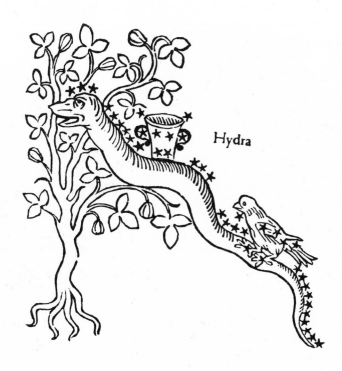

Figuration of the constellations Hydra, Crater and Corvus, engraved by Bernhard Maler, from Hyginus' *Poeticon Astronomicon,* printed by Erhard Ratdolt, Venice, 1482

~ **129**

Personification of Andromeda, from Hyginus' *Astronomicon*, Venice, 1482

eagle was considered to be a solar bird, the only being which had the power to outstare the sun. The constellation was interpreted as an eagle by all the ancient astronomers. The Hebrews called it NESHR — Eagle Vulture; the Arabs called it AL-OKAB — the Black Eagle; and to the Turks it was TAUHAUGJIL — Hunting Eagle. Its brightest star is the first-magnitude ALTAIR, from the Arabic *al-täir* — the flying bird. The second brightest star in Aquila is ALSHAIN, from the Arabic *al-shahin* — the gyrofalcon.

ARA — the Altar, from the Latin *ara* — altar, is a small, southern constellation south of the tail of Scorpio. In ancient mythological lore it was believed to be the altar of Dionysus or Bacchus. In Arabian astronomy it was called ALMIMARA, from the Arabic *al-mijmarah* — the censer. Medieval Biblical scholars and astronomers thought of it as the altar of Moses, or as the altar built by Noah after the Flood.

— the mare, because it is also the fourth brightest in Pegasus. Sometimes called the HEAD OF ANDROMEDA, it is part of the SQUARE OF PEGASUS, and of the stellar landmark of the THREE GUIDES, composed of Caph in Cassiopeia, Algenib and Alpheratz in Pegasus. The second brightest star in Andromeda is MIRACH, from the Arabic *maraqq* — the loin; and the third brightest star is a beautiful blue-orange-emerald triple star, ALMACH, from the Arabic *al-anaq* — the badger. An oval-shaped spiral nebula in the girdle of Andromeda, the LITTLE CLOUD, visible to the naked eye, has been known to astronomers since 986 A.D. It is believed to be a vast galaxy, one and a half times the size of our own.

AQUILA — the Eagle, from the Latin *aquila* — eagle, is a northern constellation in the Milky Way, south of Lyra and Cygnus. It represents the black eagle of Greek lore into which Zeus changed himself when he carried off the youth Ganymede to Mount Olympus to become the cupbearer of the gods. Among the Greeks the

Figuration of Aquilla, from Hyginus' *Poeticon Astronomicon*, Venice, 1482

ARGO NAVIS — the Ship Argo, is a huge, southern constellation in the Milky Way between Canis Major and Crux. Its name was derived from the Greek *naus* — ship, and *Argo* — the mythical fifty-oared galley of the Argonauts in which Jason and his fifty companions sought the Golden Fleece in Colchis. According to Greek legend, the ship Argo was placed in the sky by Poseidon to be forever a guide across the southern seas. In Egyptian lore it was identified with the barge in which Osiris and Isis survived the Flood, and Biblical astronomers considered it to be NOAH'S ARK. The Arabians called it AL'SUFINAS, from the Arabic *al-sufinah* — the ship. In relatively recent times it has been divided into five smaller constellations: CARINA, from the Latin *carina* — keel; MALUS, from the Latin *malus* — mast; PUPPIS, from the Latin *puppis* — stern, or poop; VELA, from the Latin *velum* — sail; and PYXIS NAUTICA — the Mariner's Compass, from the Greek *pyxis* — box, and

Figuration of Ara, from Hyginus' *Poeticon Astronomicon*, Venice, 1482

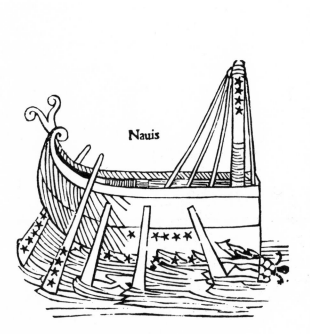

Figuration of Argo, from Hyginus' *Poeticon Astronomicon*, Venice, 1482

nautikos — sailor. The brightest star in Argo is the brilliant, first-magnitude star CANOPUS, the second brightest in the heavens. It was named after *Kanopos*, the steersman of Menelaus, king of Sparta, who died in Egypt on his return voyage from Troy and was transformed into a star. The second brightest star in the constellation is MIAPLACIDUS, from the Arabic *miyah* — waters, and the Latin *placidus* — undisturbed. Argo also contains the KEYHOLE NEBULA, one of the largest and brightest nebulae seen by the naked eye, a nebula surrounding a dark region in the form of a keyhole, with the star ARGOS in the center. This star was named after the Greek mythological builder of the ship Argo.

AURIGA — the Charioteer, from the Latin *auriga* — wagon driver, is a large, northern constellation between Perseus and Gemini. In Greek lore it represented the serpent-footed *Erechtheus*, mythical first king of Athens who invented the four-wheeled chariot because he wanted to hide his serpent-feet. Because of this invention, Zeus put him into the sky as a constellation after his death. The brightest star in Auriga, and the sixth brightest star in the heavens, is the first-magnitude double star CAPELLA — the Little She-goat, from the diminutive of the Latin *caper* — she-goat. The Assyrians called it I-KU — the Leader. The ancient Egyptians named it PTAH — the Architect, and all temples of their creator god, Ptah, were oriented to the setting of this star. The Arabs called it AL PAKIB — the Driver, because it was conspicuous in their northern sky and followed the rising of the Pleiades which Arabic shepherds thought of as a herd of sheep driven ahead of it. The second brightest star in Auriga is MENKALINAM, from the Arabic *al-mencal-i-nan* — the shoulder of the rein-holder. Three small stars which form a triangle near Capella are called the KIDS, from the Old Norse *kith* — young goat; ancient mariners believed that their rising forecast storms and cyclones.

BOÖTES — the Bear Driver, a northern constellation between Corona Borealis and Ursa Major, from the Greek *bootes* — herdsman, or plowman, was considered by the ancient astrologers to be the driver who every day chased the Great Bear around the North Pole. The brightest star in Boötes is the golden-yellow, first-magnitude ARCTURUS, from the Greek *arktos* — bear, and *ouros* — guard. It is the fourth brightest star in the heavens, and was identified in the stellar calendars as early as the 15th century B.C. It was regarded as a stormy star by astrologers, mariners and farmers alike. The second brightest star in the constellation is NEKKAR, from the Arabic *al-naqqer* — the digger.

CANIS MAJOR — the Greater Dog, from the Latin *canis* — dog, and *major* — greater, is a small, southern constellation between Lepus and

Auriga

Personification of Auriga, from Hyginus' *Poeticon Astronomicon*, printed by Erhard Ratdolt, Venice, 1482

Argo Navis. Its brightest star is the brightest star in the sky, the blue-white, first-magnitude SIRIUS, from the Greek *seirios* — scorching, also called CANICULA, or the DOG STAR, from the diminutive of the Latin *canis*. In Greek mythological legend it was considered to be the DOG OF ORION, who was transferred with his master into the heavens. The Egyptians worshiped the star and oriented the temples of Isis to it; the Arabs named it AL-KAL-AL-AKBAR, from the Arabic *al-khalb al-akhbar* — the great dog. Sirius has a satellite called the COMPANION OF SIRIUS, or the WHITE DWARF, a brilliant white star of about 26,000 miles in diameter, discovered in 1862 by the American astronomer Clark. It is a star of enormous density believed to be 3,000 times that of gold and 60,000 times that of water. It seems to be of a material composed of pure basic atoms from which all electrons have been stripped. These atoms, packed

CASSIOPEIA — the Lady in the Chair, also called the QUEEN, is a northern constellation between Andromeda and Cepheus. In Greek mythological legend, Cassiopeia was the queen of Ethiopia, wife of Cepheus, and mother of Andromeda. Because she boasted that her

CANIS MINOR — the Lesser Dog, from the Latin *canis* — dog, and *minor* — lesser, is a small northern constellation east of Orion, near Gemini. Its brightest star, the eighth brightest in the heavens, is the first-magnitude star PROCYON, from the Greek *pro* — before, and *kyon* — dog. It is so named because it rises before the Dog Star. Its second brightest star is GOMEISA, from the Arabic *ghumaysa* — Sirius.

solid, would weigh about a ton per cubic inch. The second brightest star in Canis Major is MURZIN, from the Arabic *al-mirzam* — the roarer.

boctes

Personification of Boötes, from Hyginus' *Poeticon Astronomicon*,
printed by Erhard Ratdolt, Venice, 1482

daughter's beauty was equal to that of the Ne-reids, Poseidon flooded her land and sent the sea monster, Cetus, to devour her daughter. The Arabs called the constellation ALDHAT AL-KURSITY — the Lady in the Chair. Its brightest star is the variable SCHEDAR, from the Arabic *sadr* — upper part, or breast; its second brightest star is CAPH, from the Arabic *kaff*, palm of the hand, because with four lesser stars it forms a W-shaped sign, like the lines in the palm of a hand. It is also one of the THREE GUIDES, which were used by night-traveling caravans as a celestial guide. The Danish astronomer Tycho Brahe observed, on November 12, 1572, in the constellation Cassiopeia a brilliant *supernova*, the brightest nova on record. It became as bright as Venus, visible in the daytime for nearly two years. TYCHO'S STAR, as it was called, is no longer visible today.

Personification of Cassiopeia, from Hyginus' *Astronomicon*, Venice, 1482

CENTAURUS — the Centaur, one of the largest constellations in the southern sky, lies between Hydra and Crux. It was named after the centaurs of Greek mythological legend, a mythical race of wild and coarse monsters, half man, half horse, dwelling in the mountains of Thessalia. The constellation is sometimes called PHYLLIRIDES, after the poetic name of the centaur *Chiron*. In ancient celestial charts it was depicted as carrying a spear on which the constellation Lupus was impaled. In many of these charts the centaur was changed into other kinds of animals. The brightest star in Centaurus is RIGEL CENTAURUS, from the Arabic *rijl qinturus* — foot of the centaur. It is a first-magnitude double star, the third brightest in the heavens, accompanied by a faint star PROXIMA CENTAURII, from the Latin *proximus* — the nearest, because it is the closest star to our solar system, only 4.16 light years distant. The second brightest star in the constellation, which is also the tenth brightest in the sky, is the first-magnitude AGENA. The two stars Rigel Centaurus and Agena are called the GUARDIANS OF THE CROSS or the SOUTHERN POINT-

Personification of Cepheus, from Hyginus' *Astronomicon*, Venice, 1482

ERS because a line projected through these two stars points to the Southern Cross.

CEPHEUS — the Monarch, is a southern constellation between Cassiopeia and Draco. According to Greek mythological legend, after his death, Cepheus, king of Ethiopia, husband of Cassiopeia, and father of Andromeda, was placed among the stars by the gods. Its brightest star is ALDERAMIN, from the Arabic *al-dhira al-yamin* — the right forearm, and its second brightest star ALFIRK, from the Arabic *al-firq* — the flock of sheep. There is an interesting double star marking the head of the constellation and surrounded by a dark region in the Milky Way, one of the so-called *coalsacks*; the star is named VAR CEPHEI, from the Latin *variare* — to change, because it was the first discovered star of a pulsatory type called the CEPHEIDS.

CETUS — the Whale, from the Greek *ketos*— whale, is a southern constellation between Eridanus and Aries. In Greek mythological legend it represented the sea monster sent by Poseidon to devour Andromeda and punish Cassiopeia. Its brightest star is MENKAR, from the Arabic *minkhar* — nose, and its second brightest DE-NEB KAITOS, from the Arabic *dhanab quytus* — tail of the whale. The constellation also contains a remarkable variable star with a fluted spectrum, MIRA, from the Latin *mirus* — wonderful; it is a gigantic red sun, a supergiant with a diameter of approximately 300 sun diameters and an estimated volume 30,000,000 times that of our sun.

CORONA BOREALIS — the Northern Crown, from the Latin *corona* — garland, and *boreas* — the north wind from the mountains, is a northern constellation, a cluster of seven stars in the form of a small semi-circle, between Hercules and Boötes. It was also called CORONA OF ARIADNE, representing the legendary garland given by Dionysus as a bridal gift to Ariadne of Naxos. After Ariadne's untimely death, Dionysus threw her bridal crown into the sky and Zeus changed it into a constellation.

Christian astronomers believed it to be the CROWN OF THORNS. Its brightest star is ALPHECCA, from the Arabic *al-fakkah* — to break open, and the second brightest is NUSA-KAN, from the Arabic *nasaqan* — the second in order.

CORVUS — the Raven, from the Latin *corvus* —raven, is a small, southern constellation between Crater and Virgo, standing on the back of Hydra. The Arabs called it ALGORAB, from the Arabic *al-ghurab* — the raven. The name is still used today for one of its stars.

CRATER—the Cup, from the Greek *krater*— mixing vessel, is a small, southern constellation between Leo and Corvus, standing on the back of Hydra. The Greeks called it the GOBLET OF APOLLO, and the Arabs ALKES, from the Arabic *al-ka's* — base of the bowl. This name is still used today for its brightest star.

Personification of Centaurus (Phyllirides), from Hyginus' *Astronomicon*, Venice, 1482

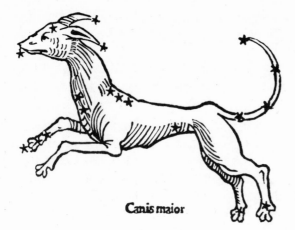

Figuration of Canis Major, from Hyginus'
Astronomicon, Venice, 1482

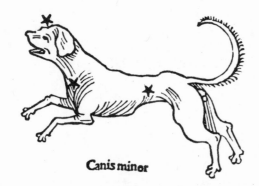

Figuration of Canis Minor, from Hyginus'
Astronomicon, Venice, 1482

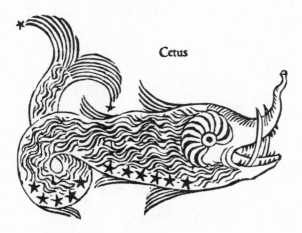

Figuration of Cetus, from Hyginus' *Poeticon
Astronomicon*, Venice, 1482

CYGNUS — the Swan, from the Latin *cygnus* — swan, is a northern constellation between Lyra and Pegasus. It is also called the NORTHERN CROSS, because six of its brightest stars form a distinct Latin cross. The constellation was named after the mythological king of Liguria, *Cycnus*, who was transformed into a swan and placed among the stars. The brightest star of the constellation is the first-magnitude DENEB, from the Arabic *dhanab al-dajajah* — tail of the hen; its second brightest ALBIREO, a blue and golden-yellow double star, from the Arabic *abireo al-dajajah* — beak of the hen; and its third brightest star is SADR, from the Arabic *sadr al-dajajah* — breast of the hen. Cygnus comprehends the NORTHERN COALSACK, the NORTH AMERICA NEBULA and the VEIL NEBULA.

DELPHINUS — the Dolphin, from the Greek *delphis* — dolphin, is a faint, small, northern constellation between Pegasus and Aquila. According to Greek mythological belief, it was the reincarnation of the dolphin that rescued the Bard of Lesbos, Arion, after he escaped from the crew of Corinthian sailors who tried to murder him for the sake of this treasures. The ancient mariners regarded the constellation as the symbolic savior of the shipwrecked. Four stars in Delphinus, forming a small rhomb, are popularly known as JOB'S COFFIN. The brightest star in the constellation is called SUALOCIN, from the reversed letters of *Nicolaus*, in memory of the Italian astronomer Nicolo Cacciatore, called Nicolaus Venator.

DRACO — the Dragon, from the Greek *drakon* — the seeing one, is a faint, northern constellation, within which is the North Pole of the ecliptic, winding its way between Ursa Major and Ursa Minor. In Babylonian astrology it was considered to be part of the Oceanic monster *Tiamat*, which was killed and halved by Bel, Babylonian chief deity, who threw one half of it into the sky and formed the earth from the other half. In Norse mythology it was the serpent

Figuration of Cygnus, from Hyginus' *Poeticon Astronomicon*, Venice, 1482

brother of Pegasus, which was given by Mercury to Castor, and was ridden by the hero on his numerous adventures. Its brightest star is KITALPHA, from the Arabic *qut'ah al-faras* — part of the mare.

ERIDANUS — the River Po, from the Greek poetic name of that river, *Eridanos,* is a long, winding, southern constellation. It starts near the foot of Orion and ends between Hydrus and Phoenix. It represents the Greek mythological river into which *Phaeton* fell from the runaway chariot of the sun after Zeus struck him down with a thunderbolt lest his careless driving set the world on fire. The brightest star in the constellation is the first-magnitude ACHERNAR, from the Arabic *akhir al-nahr* — end of the river; it is the ninth brightest star in the heavens. The second brightest star in Eridanus is CURSA, from the Arabic *al-cursa* — the footstool, so called because it is located under the foot of Orion.

Midgart, which was hurled by Odin into outer darkness. The Greek astronomers believed it to be the dragon which Juno put in the Garden of the Hesperides to guard the Golden Apples, and which was killed by Hercules in one of his twelve labors. The brightest star in Draco is ELTANIN, from the Hebrew month *elthanin* or *tishru* — the seventh month of the Hebrew calendar. The most interesting star historically is the yellow THUBAN, from the Arabic *al-thu'ban* — the dragon. Four thousand years ago it was the Pole Star revered by the ancient Egyptians, and the slanting shaft in the Great Pyramid of Khufa at Gizeh was oriented to it. In 23,000 A.D., Thuban again will be the Pole Star. The second brightest star is RASTABAN, from the Arabic *ra's al-thu'ban* — the head of the dragon.

EQUULEUS — the Little Horse, is a northern constellation between Delphinus and Aquarius near the equator. The name Equuleus was derived from the diminutive of the Latin *equus* — horse. It was also called EQUUS SECUNDUS — the Other Horse. It was said to represent the famous white horse of Greek legend, *Celeris,*

Personification of Hercules, from Hyginus' *Astronomicon*, Venice, 1482

Corona

Figuration of Corona Borealis, from Hyginus'
Astronomicon, Venice, 1482

Delpbin

Figuration of Delphinus, from Hyginus'
Poeticon Astronomicon, Venice, 1482

Figuration of Equuleus, from Hyginus'
Poeticon Astronomicon, Venice, 1482

HERCULES — the Kneeler, is a large, northern constellation between Corona Borealis and Lyra. It is named after the hero of classical Greco-Roman mythology, *Heracles-Hercules*, celebrated for his strength and for achieving twelve great tasks known as the Twelve Labors of Hercules. The Arabs called the constellation ALGETHI, from the Arabic *al-jathi* — the kneeler. Its brightest star is RAS ALGETHI, from the Arabic *ra's al-jathi* — the head of the kneeler, a beautiful, variable double star, one orange-red and the other blue-green. It is one of the largest known stars in heaven, 690,000,000 miles in diameter, or about 800 times the diameter of the sun. The second brightest star in Hercules is the golden-red double star KORNEPHORUS, from the Greek *korynephorus* — club bearer. This constellation also contains one of the finest and brightest globular star clusters in the northern hemisphere, the STAR CLUSTER OF HERCULES, which was discovered in 1716 by the English astronomer Edmund Halley (1656-1724). It is believed to comprise over 50,000 stars, each one brighter than our sun.

HYDRA — the Water Monster, from the Greek *hydra* — water serpent, is a southern constellation of great length, between Canis Minor and Centaurus. It was named after the nine-headed serpent-monster of Greek legend which lived in the marshes of Lake Lerna in the Peloponnesus, and was slain by Hercules in one of his twelve labors. Its brightest star is ALPHERAD, from the Arabic *al-fard* — the solitary one; it is also called COR HYDRAE — the Heart of the Hydra.

LEPUS — the Hare, from the Latin *lepus* — hare, is a southern constellation directly below Orion. It probably represents the animal which Orion was hunting and which was trying to hide beneath his feet. The brightest star in Lepus is ARNEB, from the Arabic *al-arnab* — the hare. It is a double star, pale yellow and gray in its components. Its next brightest star is a triple star NIHAL, from the Arabic *nihal* — thirsty. In Lepus, the English astronomer John Russell Hind (1823-1895) discovered the reddest star in the sky. It resembles a drop of blood, and today is called HIND'S CRIMSON STAR.

LUPUS — the Wolf, from the Latin *lupus* — wolf, is a southern constellation between Scorpio and Centaurus, represented in pictorial star maps by the figure of a wolf held by the hand of Centaurus. Since the Arabs called it EL-SEBU — the Animal, medieval engravers took the liberty of picturing it in the form of a goat, or some other animal.

LYRA — the Harp, from the Greek *lyra* — lyre, or harp, is a small, but important northern constellation between Hercules and Cygnus. The Akkadians called it the *Stormy Bird* or the *Vulture*, and the Chaldeans depicted it as a vulture holding a lyre. According to Greek legend it was the harp made from a tortoise shell by Hermes, given to Apollo, and played by Orpheus, son of Apollo and Calliope, the muse of epic poetry. Its brightest star is VEGA, from the Arabic *al-waqi* — the falling, the vulture. It is a brilliant blue-white star of first magnitude, the fifth brightest star in the heavens. Fourteen thousand years ago, Vega was the Pole Star, and will be the Pole Star again 12,000 years hence. The second brightest star in Lyra is the variable SHELYAK, from the Arabic *al-shalyaq* — the harp. The constellation contains the RING NEBULA OF LYRA, a galactic and typical planetary nebula in the form of an elliptic smoke ring, one of the brightest of all planetary nebulae.

OPHIUCHUS — the Serpent Holder, from the Greek *ophis* — serpent, and *echein* — to hold, also called SERPENTARIUS, is a northern constellation between Hercules and Scorpio. The Greeks considered it to be the reincarnation of *Aesculapius*, deity of medicine and healing, whose emblem was the serpent entwined around his staff. Its brightest star is the blue RAS ALHAGUE, from the Arabic *ra's al-hawi* —

cridan⁹ flumē

Personification of Eridanus, from Hyginus' *Astronomicon*, Venice, 1482

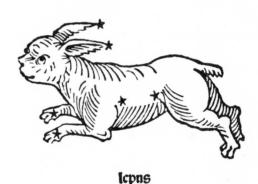

lcpus

Figuration of Lepus, from Hyginus' *Poeticon Astronomicon*, Venice, 1482

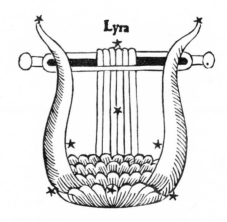

Lyra

Figuration of Lyra, from Hyginus' *Poeticon Astronomicon*, Venice, 1482

head of the serpent charmer. The constellation contains KEPLER'S STAR, a *nova* in the eastern foot of Ophiuchus, named after the German astronomer Johannes Kepler (1571-1630) who discovered it on October 10, 1604. It was the second brightest nova ever recorded and became as bright as Venus, only to fade into obscurity after about 18 months. Ophiuchus also contains BARNARD'S RUNAWAY STAR, an orange-colored dwarf star, named after the American astronomer Edward Emerson Barnard (1857-1923). It is the nearest star in the northern hemisphere, and the most rapidly moving star, traveling at a rate of 300 miles a second.

ORION — the Giant Hunter, is a southern constellation between Taurus and Canis Major. Known from earliest times, it was called in ancient Mesopotamia URU-ANNA — the Heaven-Light. In Greek mythological legend Orion was a gigantic hunter of great strength and beauty from Boeotia who was killed by Scorpio. His

body was put into heaven as a constellation by Artemis. Orion was symbolized as a giant hunter in many parts of the ancient world. In early Egypt it was the monstrous hunter SAHU who roamed the skies in search of deities whom he could rip apart and devour. The Bible called it CESIL, and the ancient Hebrews GIBBOR — the Giant. The Arabs named it ALGEBAR, from the Arabic *al-jabbar* — the giant. The brightest star in the constellation is the first-magnitude BETELGEUSE, from the Arabic *bayt al-jauza* — house of the twins, the third largest and the twelfth brightest star in the heavens. Also called the MARTIAL STAR because of its deep red-orange color, it has a calculated diameter of about 360,000,000 miles and a volume nearly 30,000,000 times that of the sun. The second brightest star in Orion is the bluish-white, first-magnitude RIGEL, from the Arabic *rijl* — foot. The third brightest star in the constellation is the pale-yellow BELLATRIX, from the Latin *bella-trix* — female warrior, also called the AMAZON

Personification of Ophiuchus (Serpentarius),
from Hyginus' *Astronomicon*, Venice, 1482

STAR, a star astrologically favorable to women. Three stars situated in a straight line form the stellar landmark BELT OF ORION, and three others the SWORD OF ORION. The constellation contains a typical dark nebula, the HORSE-HEAD, or DARK BAY NEBULA. In the hilt of the sword is the GREAT NEBULA OF ORION; modern astronomers believe that this gaseous nebula is the largest and brightest in the sky. It is 2,000 times as wide as our solar system, and about 1,200 light years away.

PEGASUS — the Winged Horse, is a northern constellation between Andromeda and Aquarius, representing the winged horse of Greek mythology which sprang from the head of the Gorgon Medusa when it was struck off by Perseus. The Arabs called this constellation AL FERAS, from the Arabic *al-faras al-azam* — the larger mare. The brightest star in the constellation is MARKAB, from the Arabic *markhab* — the saddle; in ancient astrology it was a star

of unfriendly influence, a danger to life and limb. The second brightest star in Pegasus is the variable MENKIB, from the Arabic *mankhib* — shoulder. The third brightest star in the constellation is ALGENIB, from the Arabic *al-janb* — the side, or flank; and the fourth brightest is ALPHERATZ, from the Arabic *al-faras* — the mare, also the brightest star in Andromeda. The four stars Markab, Menkib, Algenib and Alpheratz form the stellar landmark SQUARE OF PEGASUS. The stars Algenib, Alpheratz and the star Caph in Cassiopeia form the landmark THREE GUIDES. The fifth brightest star in Pegasus, ENIF, from the Arabic *al-naf* — the nose, is in reality a double star.

PERSEUS — the Rescuer, is a northern constellation between Taurus and Cassiopeia, representing the mythical Greek hero who slew the Gorgon Medusa, rescued Andromeda and turned the sea monster Cetus into stone with Medusa's head. Its brightest star is MIRFAK,

Personification of Orion, from Hyginus'
Astronomicon, Venice, 1482

from the Arabic *al-marfak* – the elbow. A star cluster in Perseus, called CAPUT MEDUSAE – Head of the Gorgon, from the Latin *caput* – head, encloses the second brightest star in the constellation, ALGOL, from the Arabic *al-ras al-ghul*—the head of the ogre. The ancient Hebrews named it ROSH-HA – the Satan. The ancients also called it BLINKING DEMON, a star with a sinister reputation, because while it shone with maximum brightness most of the time, it would suddenly decrease for a short time to minimum brightness. The ancients did not know why this star changed its light, but in the year 1783 the English astronomer Goodricke discovered that this variation in Algol is due to the eclipse of a dark star which, in passing Algol, cuts off its light from time to time. Located in the sword-hand of Perseus is a twin cluster of stars, called the STAR CLUSTER OF PERSEUS.

PISCIS AUSTRALIS – the Southern Fish, from the Latin *piscis* – fish, and *australis* –

alferas

Figuration of Pegasus (Al Feras), from Hyginus' *Astronomicon*, Venice, 1482

Perseus

Personification of Perseus, from Hyginus' *Astronomicon*, Venice, 1482

southern, is a southern constellation adjoining Aquarius. According to Greek mythological legend, it commemorates the transformation of Aphrodite into the shape of a fish when fleeing from the monster Typhon. In ancient astrology, it was believed that this constellation represented all those eager for knowledge and understanding who drank at the fountain of wisdom, since the Southern Fish lived in the waters which poured from the urn of Aquarius. Its brightest star is the first-magnitude FOMALHAUT, from the Arabic *fam al-hut* – mouth of the fish.

SAGITTA – the Arrow, from the Latin *sagitta* – arrow, is a small, northern constellation near the equator, between Cygnus and Aquila. In ancient times it was regarded as the arrow that slew the eagle of Jove.

SERPENS – the Serpent, from the Latin *serpens* – snake, is a northern constellation between Corona Borealis and Aquila, winding its way through the constellation Ophiuchus. Its brightest star is the pale-yellow and blue double star UNUK AL HAY, from the Arabic *unq al-hayyah* — the neck of the snake, also called COR SERPENTIS — the Heart of the Serpent.

TRIANGULUM — the Northern Triangle from the Greek *tri* — three, and *ankylos* — bent, is a small northern constellation between Aries and Andromeda.

URSA MAJOR — the Greater Bear, from the Latin *ursa* — she-bear, and *major* — greater, is a northern constellation between Draco and Canes Venatici. It is one of the best-known and oldest constellations, having been mentioned in the Bible (Job 9,9): *Which maketh Ash (Arctos, the Bear), Cesil (Orion) and Cimah (the Pleiades), and the chambers of the south.* In ancient Greece the constellations Ursa Major and Ursa Minor were considered as one, called ARCTOS, from the Greek *arktos* — bear. According to Greek mythological legend, the Arcadian nymph Callisto, companion of Artemis, was once masquerading as Artemis. She became pregnant by Zeus, and was changed by the enraged goddess into a she-bear; she bore a son, Arcas, and both of them were put by Zeus into the sky as the constellations Ursa. The early English called Ursa Major CHARLES' WAIN, from the Anglo-Saxon *Carles* — Charlemagne, and *waegn* — wagon. The popular English name is the GREAT DIPPER, so called from the dipper-shaped arrangement of a star group in this constellation. The brightest star in Ursa Major is DUBHE, from the Arabic *dubb al-akbar* — the greater bear. Another bright star is MERAK, from the Arabic *maraqq al-dubb*, loin of the bear. These two stars form the stellar landmark NORTHERN POINTERS, because their joining line points in the direction of the North Star. Modern astronomy has discovered in Ursa Major the OWL NEBULA, a great planetary nebula outlining the face of an owl. The German astronomer Johann Ebert Bode (1747-1826) found two ex-

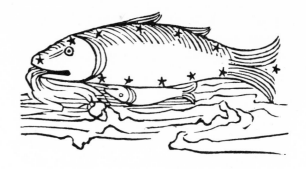

Figuration of Piscis Australis, from Hyginus' *Astronomicon*, Venice, 1482

Figuration of Sagitta, from Hyginus' *Poeticon Astronomicon*, Venice, 1482

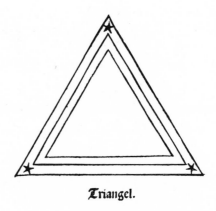

Triangel.

Figuration of Triangulum, from Hyginus' *Astronomicon*, Venice, 1482

ternal galaxies, BODE'S NEBULAE, one elliptical-spiral, and the other long, narrow and crossed by dark bands.

URSA MINOR — the Lesser Bear, located between Draco and Cassiopeia, is the most northern of all constellations. Its name was derived from the Latin *ursa* — she-bear, and *minor* — lesser; it is also called the LITTLE DIPPER, because seven stars of this constellation supposedly outline a dipper with a long handle. The early Greeks named it CYNOSURA — the Dog's Tail, from the Greek *kynos* – dog, and *oura* — tail. Its brightest star is the quadruple star STELLA POLARIS, also called the NORTH STAR, or POLE STAR, which marks the position of the celestial pole in our time. Since the axis of the earth very nearly points to the Pole Star, it seems to be almost stationary, and be-

cause from any angle in the northern hemisphere the direction north may be found by reference to it, it is one of the most important landmarks for mariners and travelers in northern latitudes. The ancient Sumerians called it ANSHAR, the god of the night sky, surrounded by his six assistants. Its Arabic name is AL KIBLAH — the Direction Star, from the Arabic *kiblah* — direction to the *Kaaba*, the Black Stone of Mecca, because it directs the Moslems, whereever they are, to turn their faces toward Mecca and the Kaaba at the hour of prayer. The English call it LODE STAR — Star of the Way, from the Anglo-Saxon *lad* — journey, and *steora* — star. The second brightest star in Ursa Minor is KOCHAB, from the Arabic *kawkab* — star; and the third brightest PHERKAD, from the Arabic *al-farqad* — the calf. The two stars Kochab and Pherkad are known as the GUARDIANS OF THE POLE.

Figuration of the constellations Draco, Ursa Major and Ursa Minor, from Hyginus' *Poeticon Astronomicon*, Venice, 1482

The Modern Constellations

ANTIOÜS — an early northern constellation between Ophiuchus and Capricorn, named after *Antinoüs,* a beautiful, voluptuous, pensive Bithynian youth who was a favorite of the Roman emperor Publius Aelius Hadrianus (76-138 A.D.). Its components are now regarded as a part of the constellation Aquila.

ANTLIA — the Pump, from the Greek *antlia* — bilge water; a small, modern, southern constellation between Argo and Hydra.

APUS — the Bird of Paradise, from the Greek *a* — not, and *pous* — foot, the Footless, because it was believed that the bird of paradise had no feet; also called AVIS INDICA — Bird of India; a modern, southern constellation between Triangulum Australe and Octans.

CAELUM — the Chisel, from the Latin *caelum* — graving tool; a modern, southern constellation between Columba and Eridanus.

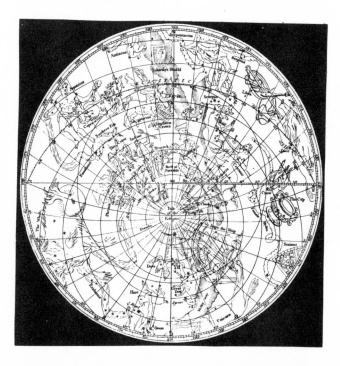

Modern representation of the Southern Celestial Hemisphere, from John Robertson's *Elements of Navigation,* London, 1805

CAMELOPARDALIS — the Giraffe, a faint, northern constellation between Cassiopeia and Ursa Major. Its name was derived from the Greek *kamelos* — camel, and *pardalis* — tiger. It was introduced in 1614 by the German astronomer Jacob Bartsch (Bartschius).

CANES VENATICI — The Hunting Dogs, from the Latin *canis* — dog, and *venatus* — to hunt, also called the GREYHOUNDS; a modern, northern constellation between Ursa Major and Boötes, found in the latter half of the 17th century by Jan Hevelius. Its brightest star is ASTERION, from the diminutive of the Greek *aster* — star, also called COR CAROLI — the Heart of Charles, in memory of Charles I of England who was executed in 1649. Its second brightest star is CHARA, from the Greek *chara* — joy. This constellation also contains the

WHIRLPOOL NEBULA, a condensed spiral nebula believed to be a very distant galaxy. The first nebula to be recognized as a spiral, it is known to astrologers as a star of evil influence called CUPOLA, from the Latin *cupola* — bond.

CHAMAELEON — the Chameleon, from the Greek *chamai* — on the ground, and *leo* — lion; a modern, southern constellation between Argo (Carina) and Octans.

CIRCINUS — the Pair of Compasses, from the Greek *kirkinos* — circle; a small, modern southern constellation in the Milky Way, next to Centaurus.

COLUMBA NOAE — the Dove of Noah, from the Latin *colombo* — dove, a modern, southern constellation adjoining Canis Major, was formed in the 16th century. It was said to be the celestial reincarnation of the dove sent out of the Ark by Noah. Astrologers considered it a harbinger of good fortune. Its brightest star, PHAET, was known and revered among the ancient Egyptians, and twelve temples were erected throughout Egypt for its worship.

COMA BERENICES — the Hair of Berenice, a small, faint, northern star cluster near Virgo, between Boötes and Leo. It was discovered by the Greek astronomer Eratosthenes of Alexandria (276-195 B.C.), and is both the first modern constellation and the first celestial body named after a real person. Its name is derived from the Greek *kome* — hair, and the name of the Egyptian princess *Barenikat,* who in 246 B.C. became Berenice II, queen of Ptolemy III. According to Egyptian legend, in obedience to a vow Berenice hung her hair in the temple of the war god, but the hair disappeared and was carried to the heavens to be changed into a constellation.

CORONA AUSTRALIS — the Southern Crown, from the Latin *corona* — garland, and *australis* — southern; a small, southern constellation below and to the left of Scorpio.

Terebellum.

The constellation Terebellum, from Leopold de Austria's *Compilatio de Astrorum Scientia,* printed by Erhard Ratdolt, Augsburg, 1491

CRUX — the Cross, also called the SOUTH-ERN CROSS, from the Latin *crux* — cross; a small, but conspicuous, modern southern constellation between Centaurus and Musca, formed by five bright stars which outline a Latin cross. It was a famous maritime guide among the early voyagers in southern seas. When Brazil was discovered in 1500 by the Portuguese navigator Pedro Alvarez de Cabral, he called the newly found land *Tierra de Vera Cruz* — Land of the True Cross. The stars of the constellation Crux are still used today in the flag of Brazil. Close beside the Southern Cross is a large dark space called the COALSACK, DARK NEBULA, or BLACK MAGELLANIC CLOUD, after the Portuguese navigator Ferdinand Magellan (1480-1521). It is believed that this dark space is due to the presence of large conglomerations of star dust which hide the star clusters lying beyond. The brightest star of the constellation, ACRUX, from the Latin *ad* — to, and *crux* — cross, was regarded by the old astrologers as the star of mysticism and occultism.

DORADO — the Goldfish, from the Spanish *dorado* — gilded, also called XIPHIAS — the Swordfish, from the Greek *xiphos* — sword; a small modern, southern constellation, embracing the South Pole of the ecliptic. It contains the NEBECULA MAJOR, from the diminutive of the Latin *nubes* — cloud, and *major* — greater. It is also called the GREATER MAGELLANIC CLOUD. This nebula, believed to be an external satellite galaxy of our galactic system, contains the super-giant star S-DORADUS, one of the most brilliant stars in our universe, with an estimated diameter of 60,000,000 miles and a brightness 316,000 times that of our sun. The cloud also contains the GREAT LOOP NEBULA, formerly called TARANTULA — the Spider, the largest irregular, gaseous nebula known.

FORNAX—the Furnace, named after *Fornax*, the Roman goddess of the oven; a southern constellation between Cetus and Eridanus.

GRUS — the Crane, from the Latin *grus* — crane; a modern, southern constellation south of Piscis Australis, added in 1604 by the German astronomer Johann Bayer.

HOROLOGIUM — the Clock, from the Latin *hora* — hour, and *logos* — telling; a faint, modern, southern constellation, formed in 1752 by the French astronomer Nicolas Louis de Lacaille.

HYDRUS — the Water Snake, from the Greek *hydros* — water serpent; a modern, southern constellation between Horologium and Octans, not to be confused with the ancient constellation Hydra.

INDUS — the Indian River, from the Sanskrit *sindhu* — river; a modern, southern constellation between Grus and Pavo, added in 1604 by the German astronomer Johann Bayer.

The constellation Vexillum, from Leopold de Austria's *Compilatio de Astrorum Scientia*, printed by Erhard Ratdolt, Augsburg, 1491

LACERTA — the Lizard, a modern, inconspicuous, northern constellation, whose name is derived from the Latin *lacertus* — lizard; formed in the latter half of the 17th century by the Polish astronomer Jan Hevelius.

LEO MINOR — the Lesser Lion, from the Latin *leo* — lion, and *minor* — lesser; a small, northern constellation between Leo and Ursa Major, added in the latter part of the 17th century by the Polish astronomer Jan Hevelius.

LYNX — the Lynx, also called the TIGER; a faint, modern, northern constellation between Auriga and Ursa Major, constructed in the latter part of the 17th century by the Polish astronomer Jan Hevelius.

MICROSCOPIUM — the Microscope, from the Greek *mikros* — small, and *skopein* — to see; a dim, modern, southern constellation south of Capricorn.

The constellation Vulture Cadens, from Hyginus' *Poeticon Astronomicon, Deutsch,* printed by Erhard Ratdolt, Augsburg, 1491

MONOCEROS — the Unicorn, from the Greek *monos* — single, and *keros* — horn; a very faint, southern constellation, situated in the Milky Way, adjoining Orion and Canis Major. It was constructed in 1624 by the German astronomer Jacob Bartsch (Bartschius).

MONS MENSAE — the Table Mountain, from the Latin *mons* — mountain, and *mensa* — table; a modern, southern constellation between Hydrus and Dorado.

MUSCA AUSTRALIS — the Southern Fly, from the Latin *musca* — fly, and *australis* — southern; a modern, southern constellation between Crux and Chamaeleon.

NORMA — the Rule, from the Latin *norma* — the carpenter's square; a modern, southern constellation between Scorpio and Triangulum Australe.

OCTANS HADLEIANUS — the Octant of Hadley; a modern, southern constellation, which includes the South Celestial Pole, formed in 1752 by the French astronomer Nicolas Louis de Lacaille. It was named in recognition of the octant, invented in 1730 by the English astronomer John Hadley.

PAVO — the Peacock, from the Latin *pavo* — peacock; a modern, southern constellation between Apus and Indus.

PHOENIX — the Phoenix, a modern, southern constellation between Grus and Eridanus, added in 1604 by the German astronomer Johann Bayer. It was named after the mythical bird of antiquity which is destroyed periodically by the fire of the sun, only to rise to new life again from the ashes, symbolizing the immortal spirit of man. Its brightest star is NAIR AL-ZAURAK, from the Arabic *nayyir al-zawraq* — the brightest star of the boat, because in early times it was part of Eridanus.

PICTOR — the Painter, from the Latin *pingere* — to paint; a dim, modern, southern constellation between Columba and Dorado, formed in 1752 by the French astronomer Nicolas Louis de Lacaille.

PISCIS VOLANS — the Flying Fish, also called VOLANS, from the Latin *piscis* — fish, and *volans* — flying; a small, modern, southern constellation adjoining Argo on the south.

QUADRANS MURALIS — the Mural Quadrant, a modern, northern constellation between Hercules and Boötes, named in honor of Tycho Brahe, who invented this astronomical instrument, no longer in use in modern astronomy.

RETICULUM — the Reticule, from the Latin *rete* — net; a modern, southern constellation between Hydrus and Dorado.

SCULPTOR — the Sculptor, from the Latin *sculpere* — to carve; a small, modern, southern constellation between Cetus and Phoenix.

SCUTUM SOBIESKII — the Shield of Sobieski, a small, modern constellation in the Milky Way between Sagittarius and Serpens. It was formed in the latter part of the 17th century by the Polish astronomer Jan Hevelius, who named it after the Latin *scutum* — shield of the Roman legions, and in honor of Jan Sobieski (John III), king of Poland (1624-1696). It contains a small, but very bright star cloud, the SCUTUM STAR CLOUD, also called the GEM OF THE MILKY WAY.

SEXTANS — the Sextant; a small, modern, northern constellation south of Leo near the equator.

TELESCOPIUM — the Telescope, from the Greek *teleskopos* — seeing from the distance; a modern, southern constellation south of Sagittarius and Corona Australis.

TEREBELLUM — the Borer, from the Latin *terebrum* — borer; an early medieval constellation, composed of a group of five stars at the tail of the Archer, now part of the constellation Sagittarius.

TRIANGULUM AUSTRALE — the Southern Triangle, from the Latin *triangulum* — triangle, and *australis* — southern; a small, southern constellation between Pavo and Circinus.

TRIANGULUM MINOR — the Lesser Triangle, from the Latin *triangulum* — triangle, and *minor* — lesser; a small, modern, southern constellation south of Triangulum Australe.

TUCANA — the American Goose, from the Tupi-Guarani *tucano* — toucan; a modern, southern constellation south of Phoenix, containing NEBECULA MINOR — the Lesser Magellanic Cloud. It is believed that this nebula is an ex-

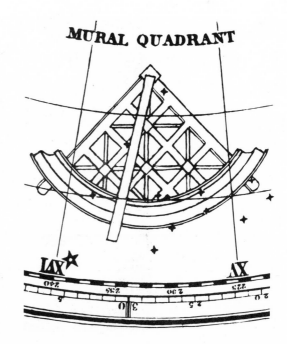

The constellation Quadrans Muralis, from a celestial atlas engraved by W. G. Evans, published by F. J. Huntington, New York, 1856

terior satellite galaxy of our galactic system, composed of 37 nebulae and 7 star clusters, with an estimated 500,000 stars.

VEXILLUM — the Flag, from the Latin *vexilla* — banner; an early medieval combination of eight stars, including parts of the constellations Leo and Virgo; no longer used in modern astronomy.

VULPECULA CUM ANSERE — the Little Fox with the Goose, from the diminutive of the Latin *vulpes* — fox, and *ansere* — goose; a small, modern, northern constellation between Sagitta and Cygnus. It was constructed in the latter part of the 17th century by the Polish astronomer Jan Hevelius, and contains the DUMBBELL NEBULA, a bright planetary, globular mass surrounded by a dark band, giving the appearance of a dumbbell.

VULTURE CADENS — the Falling Vulture, from the Latin *vellere* — to tear, to pluck, and *cadere* — to fall; an early medieval combination of stars, including parts of the constellations Antinoüs, Aquila and Sagitta; no longer used in modern astronomy.

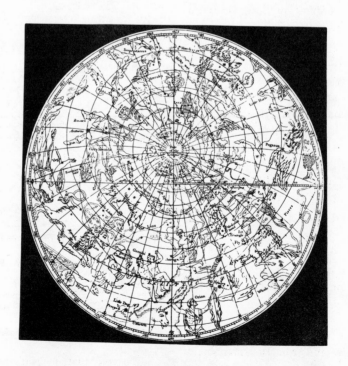

Modern representation of the Northern Celestial Hemisphere, from John Robertson's
Elements of Navigation, London, 1805

THE COMETS

Among the leisurely and orderly celestial movements of our universe, COMETS and METEORS are the erratic exceptions. Since meteors, or SHOOTING STARS, were plentiful over the years and benign in their appearance, making no particularly fearful impact on the human mind, they were not used by the ancient fate-mongers as predictive objects. Rather, they were left to the imagination of the common people, who believed them to be friendly beings, fairies or an-

gels traveling with their guiding lights through the heavens, looking for pleasant things to do and lucky feats to perform, as the wish-fulfilling servants of the common man. Meteorites, the meteors that fell to earth from time to time, were also simply explained: unconnected in the mind of the people with shooting stars they were considered to be the artillery ammunition which the celestial legions used against the satanical demons. Not so the comets. Nobody knew what

The Comet of 1066 (Halley's Comet), pictured in the Bayeux Tapestry, which is ascribed to Matilda of Flanders, queen of William I, the Conqueror (1027-1087)

Astronomical symbol for a comet,
a circle with a bearded tail

festations in the sky, flashing by like warning signals, were not the source but the harbingers of evil to come. They were considered to be bad omens of every variety of frightful future happening: of floods and droughts; of storms and earthquakes; of strife and wars; of pestilence and the Black Death; of the demise of rulers and the fall of empires. And since one or the other of these ominous things always happened somewhere in the known lands, the veiled predictions of the prophetic astrologers, that this or that comet heralded some dreadful horror to come, were generally right. In astrological tradition there are many fanciful descriptions of comets observed in bygone days. There were comets like flaming torches; winged, bearded, long-haired or pigtailed comets; comets as bright as the sun, or reaching from horizon to zenith; fearful comets shaped like, or accompanied by, swords or daggers, fans or scepters, decapitated heads or coffins; and many more.

they were, where they came from, or where they went. It is no wonder that their sudden, spectacular appearance and departure from nowhere to nowhere made a tremendous impact on the imagination; or that the superstitious mind of the people endowed these erratic celestial phenomena with a fearful and portentous significance. It was assumed that these sudden mani-

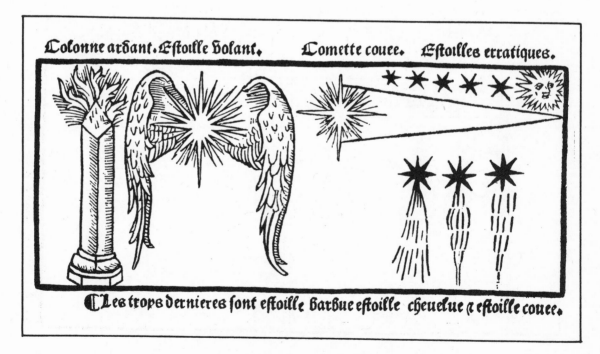

Different forms of comets, from Nicolas Le Rouge's *Le grant kalendrier
et compost des bergieres*, Troyes, 1496

The fearful Comet of 1528, accompanied by a cloud of swords, daggers, halberds and decapitated heads, from Ambroise Paré's *Livres de Chirurgie,* Paris, 1597

The artillery of the celestial legions bombarding the earth with meteorites, from a German engraving, 1628

In modern astronomy, COMETS are considered to be luminous celestial bodies, possibly originating in outer space and captured by the sun in their erratic journey through the heavens. Some are now revolving around the sun in elliptical orbits, returning at fixed intervals; others are moving in parabolas or hyperbolas, expected never to return. The name is derived from the Greek *kometes* — long-haired. A comet is composed of a starlike nucleus surrounded by a globular, nebulous mass with a long, luminous tail. METEOROIDS, from the Greek *meteoron*—thing in the air, are countless millions of solid bodies of different sizes in our solar system, traveling uncoördinately through space. They become visible METEORS on striking the earth's atmosphere—because of their high speeds they are heated to incandescence by friction with the

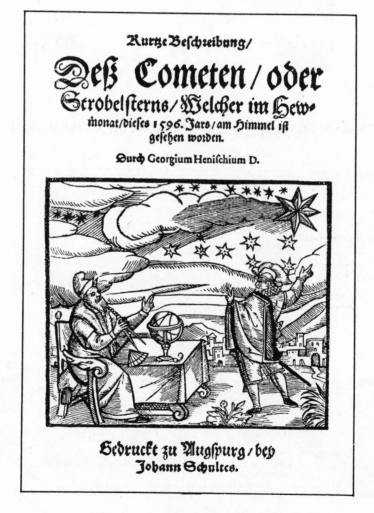

Title page from George Henischius' *Description of the Comet of 1596*, printed by Johann Schultes, Augsburg, 1596

De la Diverſité des Cometes

Different types of comets, from Mallet's *Description de L'Univers, Paris, 1683*

air. There are SHOOTING STARS, small meteors with very faint light; FIREBALLS, large, luminous meteors resembling globes of fire; and BOLIDES, brilliant, exploding meteors with trains of light or sparks, whose name is derived from the Greek *bolis* – missile. These meteors disintegrate from heat and friction in the earth's atmosphere. Some of their particles reach the surface of the earth, and are called METEORITES. These are of diversified composition and include HOLOSIDERITES, composed of kamacite, a nickel-iron-cobalt alloy without stony matter, whose name is derived from the Greek *holos* – *whole*, and *sideros* – iron; SIDERO-LITES, meteorites of a stony mixture of silicates and iron, from the Greek *sideros* – iron, and *lithos* – rock; AEROLITES, composed of silicates and very little iron, the name being derived from the Greek *aer* – air, and *lithos* – rock; URANO-LITES, stony meteorites composed solely of rock, without any iron, from the Greek *ouranos* – heaven, and *lithos* – rock; and many more. Meteorites of a substantial size are comparatively seldom seen, but the surface of the earth is bombarded day and night by COSMIC DUST, extremely small particles of meteoric matter, falling 'round the clock in enormous quantities from outer space to earth.

les conjectures du Pont Neuf, ou les effets merveilleux de la Comete vue en 1811.

The Comet of 1812, as seen from the Pont Neuf in Paris,
from a contemporary French engraving

THE ASTEROIDS

ASTEROIDS, also called PLANETOIDS, are a group of several thousands of diminutive minor planets revolving in a broad zone around the sun between the orbits of Mars and Jupiter. First detected in the course of the 19th century, they are latecomers to our body of astronomical knowledge. Their mythological names were arbitrarily selected by their discoverers. The four largest asteroids, *Ceres, Pallas, Vesta* and *Juno,* are called the BIG FOUR. All the asteroids are probably barren; they are so small that their gravity is far too weak to hold the water, gases, air or heat needed to form an atmosphere, without which not even the smallest being can exist.

CERES, the largest asteroid, with a diameter of 480 miles, was also the first discovered — in 1801 by the Italian astronomer Giuseppe Piazza (1768-1854). It was named after *Ceres,* Roman goddess of earth's vegetation, agriculture and harvest festivals. Its astronomical symbol is a stylized *Sickle of Harvest.*

PALLAS, the second largest asteroid, with a diameter of 304 miles, was found in 1802 by the German astronomer Heinrich Wilhelm Matthäus Olbers (1785-1840). It was named after *Pallas Athene,* the poetic name of the Greek goddess of wisdom and the arts of war. Its astronomical symbol is a stylized *Sword and Shield.*

VESTA, the third largest asteroid, with a diameter of 240 miles, was discovered in 1807 by the discoverer of Pallas, Olbers. It was named after *Vesta,* the Roman goddess of the hearth. The sacred fire in her temples was tended by the Vestal Virgins. Its astronomical symbol is a stylized *Hearth of Chastity.*

JUNO, the fourth largest asteroid, with a diameter of 120 miles, was found in 1804 by the German astronomer Karl Ludwig Harding (1765-1834). It was named after *Juno,* consort of Jupiter, Roman goddess of marriage, deity of the sky and the light. Its astronomical symbol is a stylized *Torch of Light.*

Symbol for Ceres
Sickle of Harvest

Symbol for Pallas
Sword and Shield

Symbol for Juno
Torch of Light

Symbol for Vesta
Hearth of Chastity

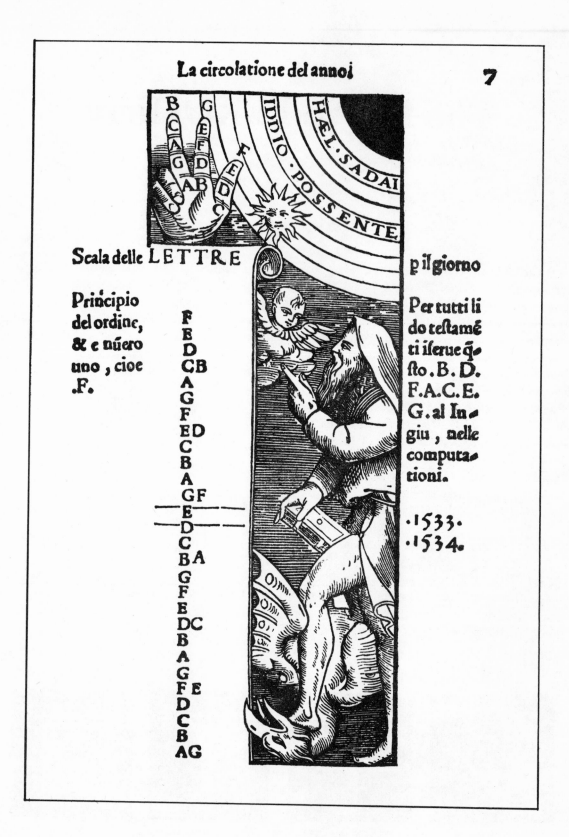

Allegoric representation of a Chaldean astrologer, from
Giovanagostin Pantheo's *Lunario perpetuo*, Venice, 1535

The Story of Astrology

ASTROLOGY, the twin sister of astronomy, was one of the prevailing forms of divination in ancient Chaldea. Chaldean astrologers had accumulated a profound knowledge of the connection between the positions of the stars in the heavens and the seasonal changes on earth, and of such natural events as eclipses of the sun and the moon and meteorological phenomena. It is only plausible to assume that with their astro-nomical and mathematical means they were sometimes able to predict some of the celestial or natural events in advance of their happening. Using their knowledge to impress and shock their fellow men, they reached exalted positions as seers in their communities and as prophets throughout their land. Astrology was unknown to the early Greeks, Egyptians and Romans. Not until the time of Alexander the Great (356-323

Arabian astrologers scanning the heavens, from Macrobius'
In Somnium Scipionis, Venice, 1513

Representation of the horoscope with the seven planets, the twelve signs of
the zodiac, and the twelve houses, engraved by Erhard Schön, from the
title page of Leonhard Reymann's *Nativitäts Kalender*, Nuremberg, 1515

B.C.) did Chaldean astrologers propagate their divinatory art of predicting man's fate from the relative astronomical positions of the stars throughout Greece, Egypt and Rome. In Republican Rome, the Chaldean astrologers, *chaldoei,* or *mathematici,* as they were called, were held in utter contempt. In 139 B.C. they became so unpopular that they were banished from Rome and Italy under pain of death. In the year 27 B.C. the first Roman emperor, Gaius Julius Caesar Octavianus Augustus, allowed the Chaldean astrologers to return, but they were forbidden to consult the stars on questions about the lives of Roman emperors. After the fall of the Roman Empire, Christian rulers prohibited all consultations with astrologers. Astrology did what is always done in times of prohibition: it went underground, and many secret forms of divination, based on astrological findings, came into being. During the gullible and superstitious Dark Ages following the fall of the Roman Empire, a number of divinatory pseudo-sciences developed in the Western world, based on the belief that the planets and zodiacal constellations in their different reciprocal positions have a profound influence on the health, fortune, character and fate of human beings. In the time of the Renaissance, astrology, with its subdivisions of *planetary al-*

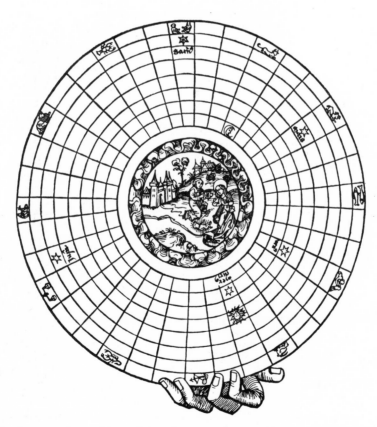

The horoscopic position of the planets and constellation at the birth of Christ, engraved by Michael Wolgemut, from Stefan Friedolin's *Der Schatz-behalter,* printed by Anton Koburger, Nuremberg, 1491

Portrait of the French astrologer and renowned soothsayer Nostradamus,
from a contemporary engraving, Paris, 1562

chemy, *Homo Signorum, chiromancy* and other forms of astrological divinations, again became presentable at the courts of the Western world. The 16th century was the golden age for astrologers, and astrology was a highly respected science. Astrologers at that time were not mere charlatans, but highly educated scholars with a broad knowledge of astronomy, mathematics and languages. There were professors' chairs of astrology and astrological medicine at many

The astrologer casting a horoscope, from Robert Fludd's *Utriusque cosmi majoris et minoris historia,* Oppenheim, 1617

European universities, such as Vienna, Wittenberg, Nuremberg and others. Rulers and their court ladies, merchants and plain people would not make decisions of any kind, without consulting beforehand their personal astrologers. The most prominent astrologer of the 16th century was the French physician Nostradamus (1503-1566), whose name is still a household word in our

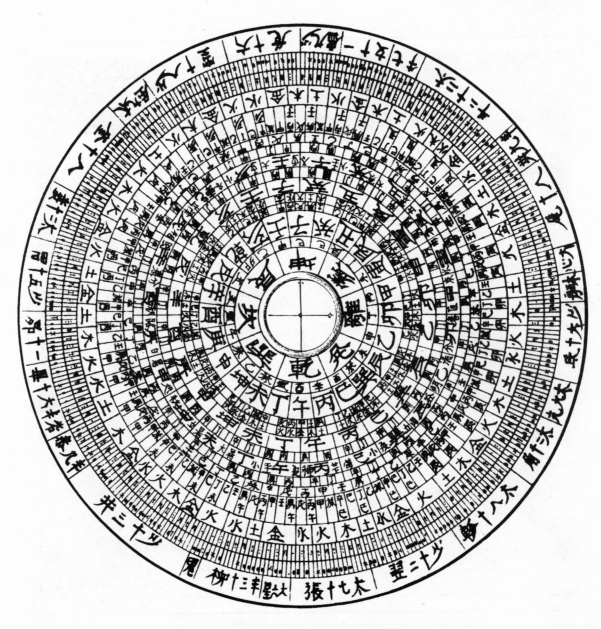

Chinese geomancer's compass, made in Hweichow, Anhwei Province, the authentic manufacturing center for this astrological instrument

time. Caesar Nostradamus, whose real name was Michel de Nostredame, was court astrologer to Catherine de Medici, queen of France. He lived in seclusion at Salon, in Provence, and wrote there his *Centuries,* each one consisting of 100 prophetic quatrains, in an obscure language still quoted today. In the Far East, astronomy, astrology, horoscopy and geomancy are intimately in-

Chinese astrologer and geomancer casting a horoscope, from an ancient Chinese drawing

terconnected, and it is impossible to determine precisely where one begins and another ends. They are all highly respected sciences, and astrological horoscopes are an important part of the daily way of life, from birth to death, for noble and humble men alike. In Chinese mythological lore, *Fu-Hsi* (2953-2838 B.C.), the first divine emperor of the Legendary Period, constructed the *Pa-Kua*, or Eight Diagrams, revealing all the mysteries of the heavens. He gave to mankind the knowledge of divination from the elements, the planets and the stars. For every event in the life of an Oriental, and for every decision in his business or profession, a horoscope is needed to decide the best year, month,

day and hour for the undertaking. In China not only the auspicious day and hour for the burial of a deceased person are determined by an astrologer, but also the best spot for the burial plot is chosen by a geomancer in accordance with the horoscope of the deceased. There are no Chinese cemeteries in our Western sense; Chinese burial grounds belong to the clan or village, or are the graves of the family house; and such graves can be found scattered anywhere over the landscape. In the Western world today, any kind of divination is belittled and sneered at. But notwithstanding that fact, astrology is still a thriving business of gigantic proportions on both the European and American continents.

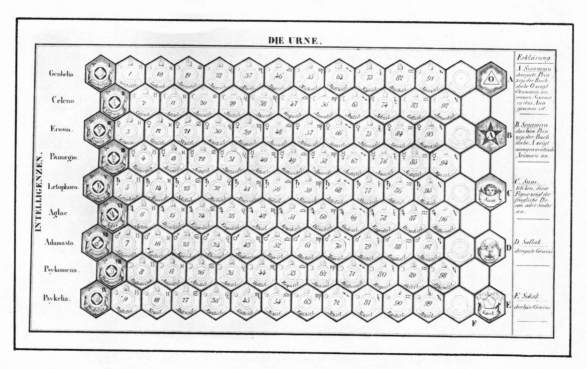

The *Urn of Zoroaster*, a mechanized horoscopic chart of inscribed wooden hexagons, fitted together to determine the good or bad influence of the star spirits, from Scheible's *Das Kloster*, Stuttgart, 1846

HOMO SIGNORUM

One of the outstanding doctrines of bygone days was the belief that the planets and the signs of the zodiac exerted a powerful influence on certain parts of the human body. The origin of this belief is lost in the haze of unrecorded antiquity, but it was already known to the Romans of the pre-Christian era who may have borrowed it from the ancient Greeks. It was referred to in Christian manuscript calendars of the 2nd century A.D., in which all kinds of astronomical and astrological data were compiled *(Ephemerides)*. The pictorial representation of this doctrine, the figure of a man or a human skeleton surrounded by the twelve signs of the zodiac or the seven symbols of the planets in their relation to the human body, appeared first in the manuscripts of the 14th century. It was called HOMO SIGNORUM — the Man of Signs, MOON'S MAN, or ANATOMY. In the Dark Ages, in medieval medicine, and as late as the last century, the

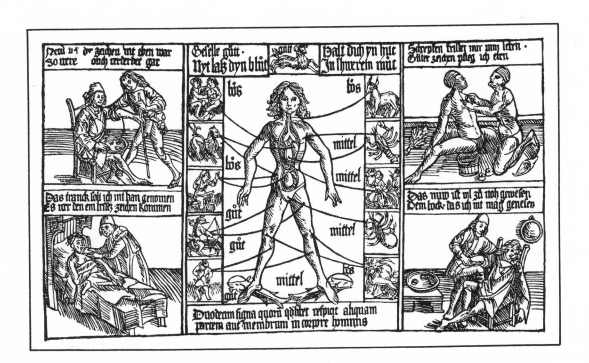

Astrological bloodletting and cupping chart, used
by barber-surgeons as fair posters, Germany, 1480

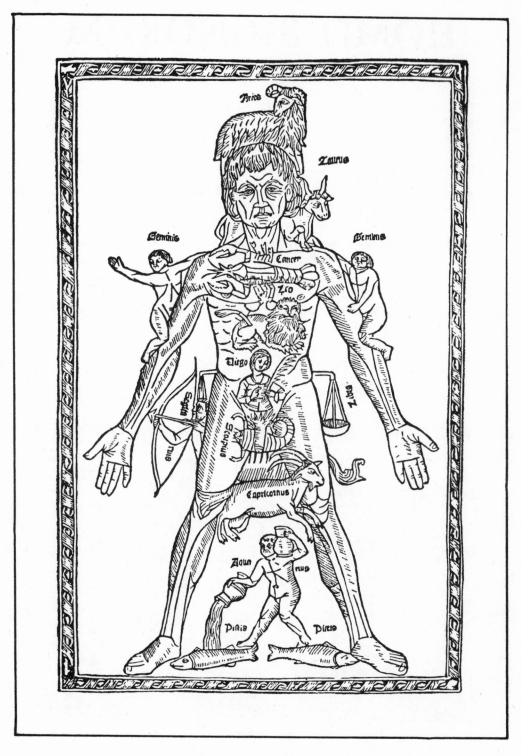

Homo Signorum — the Man of Signs, from *Epilogo en medicina*, printed by Juan de Burgos, Spain, 1495

astrological relations among the sun, the moon, the planets and the zodiacal constellations governing the afflicted parts of the human body, were part and parcel of every medical and surgical decision. The influence of the celestial bodies was so important for a surgical operation that an exact knowledge of the astronomical position of the planets and constellations was necessary

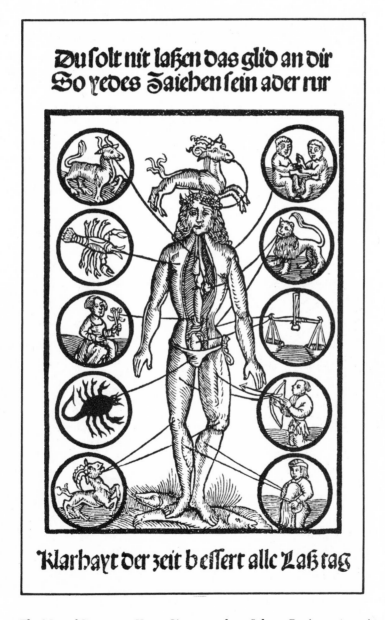

The Man of Sorrow as *Homo Signorum*, from Johann Regiomontanus' *Kalendarius teütsch*, printed by Johann Sittich, Augsburg, 1512

to determine the best day for such an undertaking. In the language of the *Shepherd's Calendar*, an English translation of the earlier French *Grant kalendrier des bergieres*, printed at London in 1506 by Richard Pynson:

a man ought not to make incysyon ne touche with yren ye membre gouerned of any sygne the day that the mone is in it for fere of to grete effusyon of blode that myght happen, ne in lykewyse also when the sonne is in it, for the daunger & peryll that myght ensue.

From the 15th to the 19th centuries, PHLEBOTOMY (from the Greek *phlebos* — vein, and *temnein* — to cut), the practice of bloodletting, was one of the most important medical treatments, prescribed as a cure-all for every kind of ailment and disease. The knowledge of the as-

trological influence of the celestial bodies on the different parts and organs of the human body became an axiomatic necessity for medical science. *Homo Signorum* — the Man of Signs, *L'Homme Phlébomatique* — the Man of Bloodletting, and the *Aderlass Tafeln* — Bloodletting Charts, were the most popular illustrations in books of the hours, natural histories, medical treatises and farmer's almanacs of that time. Even the traveling barber-surgeons, who put up their shingles at city fairs and country markets, posted broadsides of bloodletting charts in front of their stalls and tents to inform the strolling passers-by about the best day and time to come in for a bloodletting or cupping glass treatment for their special ailments. Diagrams of the Man of Signs are still published in some of our contemporary almanacs.

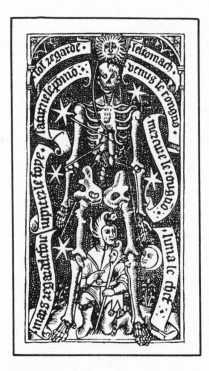

L'Homme Phlébotomique as skeleton, from
Le Rouge's *Grant kalendrier*, Troyes, 1496

L'Homme Phlébotomique, from Godard's
Heures, by Nicolas Hygman, Paris, 1518

PLANETARY ALCHEMY

As astrology was the forerunner of astronomy, so was alchemy the precursor of chemistry. And alchemy, like every other ancient philosophical science, was deeply influenced by its astrological aspects. In ancient Chaldean belief the planets were associated with the alchemical metals. The Greeks accepted the belief that the sun symbolized gold and the moon silver. The planet Aphrodite-Venus represented copper; Hermes-Mercury, quicksilver; Ares-Mars, iron;

Zeus-Jupiter, zinc; and Cronus-Saturn, lead. When in the 4th century B.C. Greek philosophers settled in Alexandria, the center of learning at that time, they introduced planetary alchemy to the Egyptians along with all their other scientific knowledge. In the Dark Ages in Europe this knowledge was lost, but in the 8th century A.D. the Arabic alchemist Abu-Musa Dschabir, called Geber, taught the ancient Chaldean beliefs to his Arabic pupils. With the spread of the Islamic

Alchemists & the planetary metals, engraved by Dominico Beccafumi di Pace (1486-1551), Italy

Fons Mercuralis — the Fountain of Life, from *Rosarium Philosophorum,* Frankfort/M., 1550

~ 171

The *Alchemic Sky Dragon* linking the sun and the moon, engraved by
V. Feil, from Hanns Singriener's *Vögelin Praktik*, Vienna, 1534

Empire throughout the following centuries, planetary alchemy was propagated along the Mediterranean Sea, and reached from the Arabic strongholds in Sicily and Spain into the mainland of western Europe. The astrological-alchemical belief of the Chaldeans, Babylonians, Assyrians,

A discussion between the sage and the scholar under the *Hermetic Tree of Knowledge*, from Basile Valentin's *L'Azoth des Philosophes*, Paris, 1659

Greeks, Romans, Egyptians and Arabs was that the heavenly bodies dominated all earthly things. This was accepted by the medieval European alchemists and metallurgists as natural law; and the astronomical symbols also became the alchemical symbols of the basic metals. In medieval times every ruler sponsored his own personal court alchemist whose experiments dealt primarily with the ultimate goal of discovering the *Philosopher's Stone*, an imaginary substance which, under certain favorable planetary conditions, would change the basic metals into gold and silver. Thus the alchemist's protector would be able to afford for his conquests and reprisals a bigger and stronger army than his adversaries.

At the time of the more sophisticated Renaissance, the alchemists branched out into the search for more philosophical goals — such as the legendary *Fons Mercuralis* — the Fountain of Mercury, which spouted the elixir of perpetual youth, a belief derived from the Biblical "Rivers of living waters" (New Testament, John 7,38) and the Islamic "Spring of life" (The Koran, Sura 18); or the *Planetary Tree of Knowledge*, an hermetic image of the soul, the spirit, and the body of the universe; or *Hermaphroditus*, the male-female principle of alchemic transmutation, personified by the son of the Greek mythological gods Hermes and Aphrodite who became joined in body with Salmacis, the nymph of the

Hermaphroditus straddling the winged globe of chaos, from Jamsthaler's
Viatorium Spagyricum, Frankfort/ M., 1625

Fountain of Caria; or the *Alchemic Sky Dragon,* by whom the sun and the moon were swallowed and reborn every day, and which was the symbol of the eternal nature of *materia prima* — the first matter, or indestructible basic material of the universe; and so on. Notwithstanding the fact that the aims of ancient alchemy were not scientific, alchemists, in their quest for knowledge and in their untiring experimentation with every kind of material they could find — mineral, animal or vegetable — made many useful discoveries which were of basic value to modern chemistry, metallurgy and pharmacology.

The *Mountain of the Adepts,* containing the *Philosopher's Stone,*
from Stephan Michelspacher's *Alchemia,* 1654

CHIROMANCY

CHIROMANCY, from the Greek *cheir* — hand, and *mantis* — prophet, the art of telling fortune and future from the lines and mounts of the human hand, which are believed to be under the astral influence of the planets and the zodiacal signs, was a medieval pseudo-science. While astrology, with its involved calculations founded in antiquity on extensive astronomical knowledge, was predominantly a masculine science practiced by astronomers, physicians and other learned men, chiromancy was developed by medieval soothsayers and occultists, and with its ever-changing, unscientific rules based on intuitive reflections and predictions, soon became the domain of female fortune-tellers, gypsies, and witches. According to chiromantic belief, *Pollex* — the thumb, is influenced by Venus, and the adjacent *Mons Veneris* — the Mount of Venus, predicting love and harmony, is surrounded by the Venusian or Life Line. *Index* —

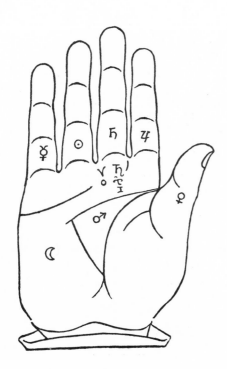

Oldest print of right hand planetary positions, from Ratdolt's *Chiromantia*, Venice, 1480

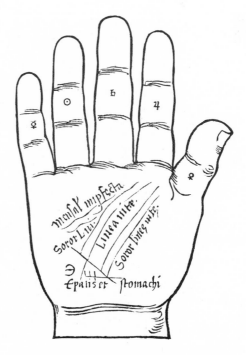

Planetary positions in the right hand, from de Indagine's *Chiromantia*, Strassburg, 1531

~ **175**

the forefinger, assigned to Jupiter, is the starting point of the Jovian or Heart Line, and *Mons Jovis* — the Mount of Jupiter, denotes independence and ambition. *Medius* — the middle finger, dedicated to Saturn, is the starting point of the Saturnian or Fate Line, and *Mons Saturnus* — the Mount of Saturn, is the gauge of seriousness.

Annularis — the ring finger, influenced by the sun, is the fountain of the Apollonian or Solar Line, the line of fortune. *Mons Solis* — the Mount of the Sun, also called the Mount of Apollo, reveals the capacity for brilliance, arts and sciences. The mounts of Saturn and the Sun are encircled by *Cingulum Veneris* — the Girdle of

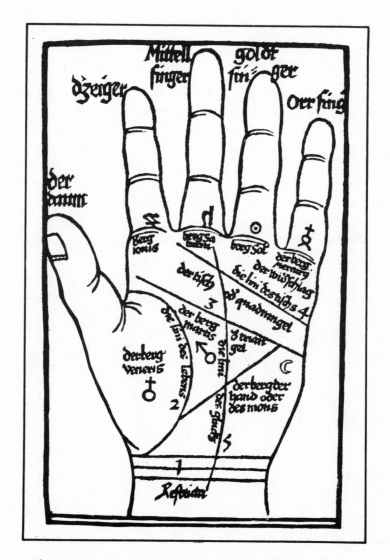

Planetary positions in the left hand, from Bartholomeus Cocle's
Chiromantiae Compendium, Strassburg, 1551

Venus, a line disclosing intemperance and lust. *Auricularis* — the little finger, is the domain of Mercury, the starting point of the Mercurian or Health Line, and *Mons Mercurii* — the Mount of Mercury, foretells the strength of practicality. *Cavea Martis* — the Caves or Plains of Mars, located in the center of the palm, cut through by the Martian or Head Line, are the prediction source of aggression, courage and temper. *Locus Luna* — the Place of the Moon, also called *Mons Manus* — the Mount of the Hand, situated at the percussion edge of the palm below the little finger, contains the marks of imagination and melancholy. It is bisected by *Via Lactea* — the

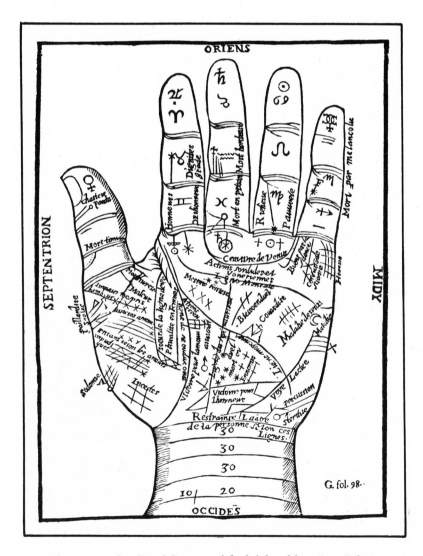

Planetary and zodiacal diagram of the left hand from Jean Belot's
Oeuvres Diverses, Lyons, 1649

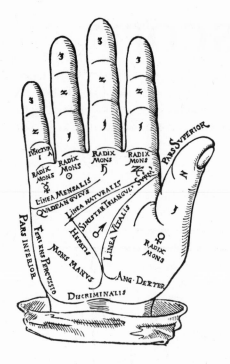

Planetary positions in the right hand, from T. de Cerasari's *Principium Chiromantiae*, Nuremberg, 1560

Milky Way or Line of Happiness. The joints of the fingers were believed to reveal the influence of the signs of the zodiac, read from the tip to the base of the fingers: on the forefinger the *intellectual signs* of Aries, Taurus and Gemini; on the middle finger the *serving signs* of Capricorn, Aquarius and Pisces; on the ring finger the *maternal signs* of Cancer, Leo and Virgo; and on the little finger the *reproductive signs* of Libra, Scorpio and Sagittarius. The chiromantic belief that the astral influence in a person's life, character and fate is visible in the lines and mounts of his hands, remained strong throughout the centuries. The art of chiromancy, or *palmistry*, as it is called today, is still a thriving business in our tea rooms and on the midways and boardwalks of our fairs and watering places.

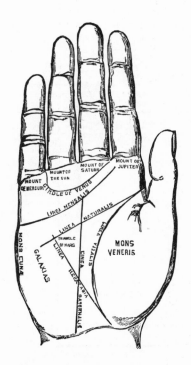

Planetary mounts and lines of the right hand from Wehman's *Witches' Dream Book*, New York, 1885

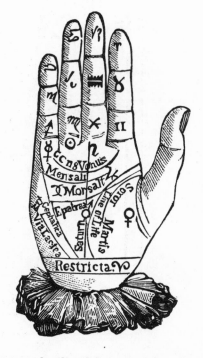

Planetary and zodiacal diagram of the right hand, from Wehman's *Witches' Dream Book*, New York, 1885

METOPOSCOPY

METOPOSCOPY, from the Greek *metopon* — forehead, and *skopos* — watcher, is the occult technic directed toward the evaluation of a person's character and fate from the lines on his forehead. French and Italian occultists of the 17th century developed the theory that the wrinkles and lines of the human forehead presented an unfailing chart of the relations between the planets and the good and bad characteristics of a person. There are, in theory, seven principal lines on the human forehead. Reading from the brows upward they are the lines of the Moon, Mercury, Venus, the Sun, Jupiter and Saturn. Very few persons possess all seven lines. Their presence or absence, their straight, wavy, erratic or broken appearance, give the metopomancer the means to deduce the character and fate of the observed subject. Metoposcopy is very seldom practiced in our time.

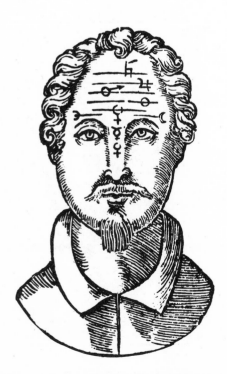

Position of the planets on the human forehead, from Ciro Spontoni's *Metoposcopia,* Venice, 1637

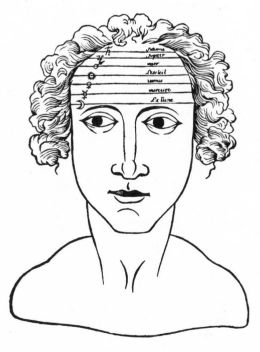

Position of the planets on the human forehead, from Jerome Cardan's *Metoposcopia,* Paris, 1658

~ 179

CARTOMANCY

CARTOMANCY is divination or fortune-telling by means of a deck of cards, called *tarots*. In the 14th century these playing cards and the art of cartomancy were brought from the Near East to Italy by a nomadic people, believed to be Egyptians, or *Gypsies,* a name abridged from *Egypcyans*. But in reality these people came from India and called themselves *Romany,* a name derived from the Sanskrit *doma* — a wan-

dering musician of low caste. The origin and meaning of the tarots are Oriental, but they became popular in the 15th century in Venice, Lombardy, France, Austria and Hungary. Later on they became known from Russia and Turkey to Spain and England, and even on the American continents, wherever the wandering Gypsies went. There are ancient tarot decks with cards of astrological meaning, such as the cards from

The Sphere of the Fixed Stars, and the Sun as the Main Movable
Star, astrological tarocchi from a 15th-century Italian deck

The Stars, the Moon, the Sun and the Earth, tarot cards
from a 19th-century French deck

the *tarocchi di Mantegna:* tarot cards with the signs of the zodiac, or with astrological forecasts. There is the Card of the Stars, No. 17, the symbol of hope; the Card of the Moon, No. 18, forecast-ing danger; the Card of the Sun, No. 19, standing for happiness; and the Card of the World, No. 21, representing the symbol of success.

Allegory of Astrological Cartomancy, engraved by Joseph Porta Garfagnino, from *Le Sorti di Francesco Marcolini da Forli,* printed in Venice, 1540

List of Illustrations

~ **185**

Tailpiece with stellar ornament, from Giulio Strozzi's
La Venetia edificato, Venice, 1624

~ **187**

INDEX

Page references in italics refer to illustrations

~ **189**

Emblematic representation of the sun, from Juan de Horosco y Covarrubias'
Emblemes Morales, printed by Juan de la Cuesta, Segovia, Spain, 1589